# How's your Prostate?

# How's your Prostate?

## A Cancer Survivor's Candid Journey

Kenneth D. Michaels, MEd

LA MANCHA PRESS

Published by La Mancha Press.



Contact Kenneth D. Michaels at:
Kenneth.Michaels03@gmail.com
www.kennethdmichaels.com

Cover Design by Laura Duffy
Book Design by Karen Minster
Author photograph by Carol Tedesco
Cover and title page photograph
by John Wollwerth/Shutterstock

ISBN 978-0-9983242-4-1 (paperback)
ISBN 978-0-9983242-5-8 (e-book)

LCCN 2018910933

Printed in the United States of America

For Shelli and Butch,
and for all those who have been
touched by this disease

# Contents

## Author's Note

The treatments and other medical choices described in this book reflect the prostate cancer medical options available in 2008. There have been many changes since then and much new research.

Early warning signs of prostate cancer may include trouble getting or maintaining an erection, pain while urinating, and/or blood in your urine. Insist on a blood test and urinalysis. Your treatment choices should result from careful evaluation following consultation with your physician.

So I could be free to write candidly about my experiences, names have been changed in the story that follows, with the exception of family members and close friends.

# How's your Prostate?

# 1. Premature Retaliation

I spilled the coffee grounds, put jam on my cereal, and buttered the dog, all while trying to find Dr. Strong's telephone number. He was my GP and the voice of reason. Right now, I knew I was unreasonable. I watched the clock ... He didn't get in until nine, and it was only seven ... *Tick-tock, tick-tock* ... I was afraid I had cancer, prostate cancer to be exact. *Tick-tock, tick-tock.* It was 9:01, and I finally reached Dr. Strong, my rock.

"This is Dr. Strong. How can I help you?"

"I have cancer. I know I'm dying. I need your help."

I felt my world had collapsed. I wanted to scream as loudly as I could, but I didn't want to wake the neighbors. I think I may have been insane then. In fact, I'm sure of it. And, here's the kicker: I'm a therapist. That's right, a psychotherapist. You may be thinking, *Boy, does he have issues.* Many therapists *do* have issues. I think that's a reason I became one, hoping to resolve my own problems. That didn't work, and eventually I did see a therapist.

Enough of that. *Shhh*, Dr. Strong was on the phone now.

"Why do you think you have cancer?" he asked calmly.

"My PSA test was 3.6. It's never been that high."

PSA is a prostate-specific antigen, a protein produced by the prostate gland, measured by a blood sample sent to a lab. A high score may indicate the presence of prostate cancer. The Mayo Clinic claims "about 80% reliability," with the qualifier that "one out of five men may go undetected."

I believe that early detection may have saved my life, and without it I may not be writing this today. I knew my score because the week before, Dr. Bark had given me a full physical. I would have preferred my usual GP, but Dr. Strong had been unavailable. At seventy-eight, he resembled a grandfather in a Rockwell print. Dr. Bark was young. Maybe he didn't know how to read results. That's called "magical thinking" in the psych world.

A PSA score is either high or it isn't. Of course, there are false positives and true negatives, which only made me crazier, because no one knows exactly why. I did know it meant I would need a few more readings before making any final decisions about my cancer. But I was sure I had cancer. I was positively negative.

"There are many reasons it may be high. You'll have to rule those out first," Dr. Strong said.

"Like what?" I asked.

"A urinary infection, low white cells, a cold."

"Really?"

"Yup."

"Mmmm," I mumbled, not quite convinced.

"And it ain't cancer 'til it's cancer. Who told you it's cancer?" he asked.

"Dr. Ego."

I consulted with Dr. Ego, a psychiatrist, on a weekly basis, to gain insight about my patients. Occasionally, well, more than occasionally, I'd talk about myself. It was a bargain, a twofer, so to speak. I had seen him the day before, and he had informed me that he was taking a two-week vacation. How dare he leave when I needed him? I secretly hoped he'd ski into a tree.

"He's not an oncologist or a urologist. You need to get a biopsy, and even if it's cancer, you have options. Besides, it is one of the slowest-growing cancers there is. You have time to make decisions. Calm down and arrange another reading. If it's still high, you should get a biopsy. You'll be fine. Do you hear me?"

"Yes," I said.

"Good. Call Dr. Hartless. Mary will give you the number. Let me know what happens, and good luck." I felt a little calmer. I made my appointment with Dr. Hartless and prayed for the best.

Apparently, I had said the wrong prayers. Dr. Hartless wasn't available, but his resident, Dr. Bolt, was. He stuck a lubed, latexed finger up my butt and squeezed my prostate roughly, prompting a spontaneous ejaculation onto a glass slide. Ironically, this torture was known as a prostate massage—but by no stretch of the imagination was it pleasurable. This was followed by another PSA test, which, when compared to my first score of 3.6, might rule out other problems.

I started to have a panic attack as soon as I left the office. As a psychotherapist, I have dealt with patients who were experiencing pain, grief, and anxiety. Never did I think I would be dealing with all of these emotions at the same time.

Two days later the results were in. The good news was I didn't have any STDs; the bad news was that my second PSA score was 7.1. I wondered whether my condition was genetic, if the lab was inaccurate, or if my lifestyle had changed. I couldn't answer any of those questions, so I decided to pray even more and be kinder to my fellow man.

## 12/16/07: Making an Appointment for My Biopsy

I decided to call for a biopsy appointment the next day.

"I need an appointment."

"That's obvious. You've called three times in the last hour," the receptionist said.

*Great*, I thought, *I get Satan's gatekeeper.*

"If it was that obvious, you should have called me back the first time," I said, trying not to be intimidated even though I was.

"Policy states you must wait a month after your last PSA test before we schedule a biopsy, and you just had one yesterday," she said, not skipping a beat.

"I'd rather not wait a month. I could have cancer," I said.

"Policy," she stated. A cold, flu, cancer. It was all the same to her. She had power or thought she did. As a psychotherapist, I'd dealt with this before. I could see right through her. Lonely and insecure.

"For you, there's a sublet in hell," I muttered.

"What did you say?"

"You're clear as a bell," I corrected myself. When angry, I often let my real feelings slip through, but she didn't hear my annoyance.

"Policy," she repeated.

There was no point arguing. She was told to follow procedure and POLICY, and there was no way around it. I knew it was pointless to try to go over her head. If my PSA was as low as the level of efficiency and charm she showered on me, I would have been the happiest man in Chicago and one with options. But most likely, there would be more appointments, and I didn't have the luxury of alienating the gatekeeper of my future.

"I have an opening on Friday, January fifteenth, at two p.m. with Dr. Hartless."

"I'll take it," I said, and immediately recited the Serenity Prayer.

*God grant me the serenity*
*to accept the things I cannot change;*
*courage to change the things I can;*
*and wisdom to know the difference.*

I also knew the holidays were approaching rapidly, and if I didn't set up an appointment now, it would only be delayed further.

## 1/15/08: The Biopsy

A month later, I was brought into an office, told to get into a gown, and then forced to wait over an hour. I read a *Time* magazine ("Federal Deficit Soars"), then *Newsweek* ("Obama's Campaign Surges"), and thought, *Will the federal deficit stop soaring or Senator Obama's campaign stop surging while I worry about having cancer?* I was getting myself into a state.

Next, I stared at an illustrated poster of the penis. I followed the urethra, a pipeline of sorts that started in the penis highway, which led to the prostate, just below the bladder. I was trying not to get it confused with the vas deferens, another pipeline, which led from the testes on another highway over the bladder to the seminal vesicle, which also led to the prostate gland. It was a urinary GPS for those of us who are medically challenged.

"Sorry for the delay," the doctor said as he entered the room, startling me. I was so focused on looking at the complicated connections to the prostate gland, I nearly fell off the examination table. "I'll get your chart and be back in a minute."

A few minutes later, as I knelt on the table with my butt fully exposed, I thought, *He didn't even bother to introduce himself. That's cold.* But that was nothing. When he pushed a scope up my butt, I cringed. Now, *that* was COLD.

Then Dr. Hartless said, "This is going to pinch a bit. I'm giving you a topical anesthetic, but you'll still feel the procedure." Pressure, more pressure, click, and snip. *AAYEE.* An excruciating, unbelievably long click and snip. *UUYAA.*

"Okay. That was the first sample. We only have fifteen more to go."

I thought I'd die from PAIN. This was unfair. Why wasn't I sedated for this? There must be another way. MORE PAIN. There had to be some sort of drugs. TEARS OF PAIN. Was this really necessary? He was a S-A-D-I-S-T. What did I ever do to deserve this? And then, it was over.

"That wasn't so bad, was it?"

Before I could respond, he said, "You might urinate and ejaculate blood for a couple of days, but don't be alarmed. That's normal. I'll be out of town for the next two weeks, vacation. Results should be back in three days, but I don't expect anything out of the ordinary."

As he ripped off his gloves, washed his hands, and opened the door, he turned. "Any questions?"

I wanted to jump off the table and strangle him, but before I could finish that thought, he had already left, shutting the door behind him. I noticed that the front of my paper gown was wet. It could have been from anything, but I saw a drop of water fall from my chin. Then another. I realized I was still crying. Fear, anger, exhaustion. It didn't matter. I got dressed and left the office, feeling violated and ashamed as I started my walk of pain back home.

Since that time, I have talked to a number of men and learned that the doctor decides whether the patient should be hospitalized or not. It is totally subjective. It rarely has anything to do with accuracy, I was told. Many of us have had biopsies by insensitive urologists, and granted, each person is different, but there are some similarities. Pain, approach, explanation. Some urologists seem dispassionate about the side effects of a prostate biopsy. I know I was shocked at the amount of blood I found in my urine and semen for nearly a month. Once I learned that not all urologists are that insensitive and sadistic, I fired mine.

Hopefully, my journey will provide you or your loved ones with some useful information that will allow for more educated choices. I would also suggest another option that would allow the patient to be premedicated before coming to the office with the caveat that he must have someone drive him to and back from the appointment.

## 1/18/08: Three Days Postbiopsy, First Call

I called Dr. Hartless's office. After a few rings, I was connected to a recording: "You have reached the offices of Hartless and

Associates: For hours, press 1; location, press 2; for appointments, press 3; for all other questions, press 4." I pressed 4 and listened to silence.

I was ready to give up and start again when I heard an efficient and hurried voice say, "Can you hold?"

It was my lucky day. A response on my first try, and I was "on hold." Silence. Waiting. *Click, click, click,* dial tone. "Premature satisfaction," I mumbled. "How annoying."

I tried again and got a repeat performance of: "You have reached the offices of ..." and I knew that I should press 4 for all other calls. I waited (what was my choice?) and then was asked again, "Can you hold?"

Before I could react, I heard, "We are experiencing an extreme number of calls. If you like, you can leave your name and number, and we'll get back to you as soon as possible. Wait time is seventeen minutes."

I knew that leaving a message was useless. I decided to be mature and screamed, "I hate holding. I hate your office. I hate you."

I've heard that sometimes the line is open and office personnel can hear your complaints. Even worse, I have heard that the staff laughs at these outbursts and often disconnects without any conscience. Realizing the futility of my anger, but furious anyway, I threw the phone at the wall as hard as I could. Given the stated wait time, I opted to run to the bathroom.

Just as I unzipped and started, from the receiver lying across the room, I heard, "How can I help you?" Pause. "Hello ... ? These people really know how to waste my time," the voice said. I knew from her tone she would disconnect within seconds.

I lunged for the phone, my penis dangling precariously, much too close to my zipper. "I'm here. Don't hang up. I'm here." I grabbed the receiver and held on to it as if I had recovered a crucial fumble. I was out of breath and dripping.

"Yes," I said, which made no sense, but I was talking to a live person. I might even score. "I'm calling about my biopsy results," I said.

"Next time, stay on the phone if you want some help."

"I'm sorry ..." (I wasn't.)

"Name, doctor, procedure?" she rattled off.

"You see, I was in the bathroom and—"

"I don't care. Name, doctor, procedure," she repeated, following with a long sigh.

"Michaels, Hartless, biopsy," I replied rapidly. I had learned that I had to be prepared or suffer the consequences. I waited with anticipation.

"The doctor is with a patient."

"I thought he was on vacation."

"I said, Dr. BamBam is with a patient."

"Dr. Hartless is my doctor."

"Why didn't you say so?"

"I did."

"No, you didn't. I know the difference between BamBam and Hartless. Hartless is on vacation. I have a lot of calls. I'm very busy."

"I know. I know. Dr. Hartless told me to call for the results of my biopsy after three days, and—"

Before I could finish my sentence, I was interrupted with, "Can you hold?"

"No, no, no. I can't." And I realized I was talking into a void. I hit the wall repeatedly until my hand hurt and then ran it through what little hair I had left. Then I banged my head against the wall.

The voice returned. "Mrs. Prentiss, Dr. Slow wants you to come in for another colposcopy. He found some anomalies in your vagina."

I let this sink in and then yelled, *"This is Ken Michaels. I don't have a vagina, and I want my b-b-biopsy results!"* On the verge of rage, I stuttered, something I sometimes do.

"I have an opening on January twenty-first at three."

"All I want are my biopsy results. I need to know if I have cancer."

"Everyone needs to know if they have cancer, Mr. Michaels. Dr. BamBam is very busy, and there are a lot of people who want to see him. Do you want the appointment or not?"

"No," I said. "I mean yes, but—"

"It's your funeral," she said, and hung up.

I hadn't reached a person. I had reached the Angel of Death. I didn't have any more energy to continue. I called it a day and fell asleep on the floor.

The next day, I called and reached the answering service.

"The office doesn't open until nine a.m." I looked at my watch. It was 9:10. I was trying to figure out this contradiction. Then she said, "Would you like to leave a message?"

I left my information, and when I hadn't heard from anyone by eleven a.m., I called the office again. This time I managed to reach a nurse by pressing the star key repeatedly.

They weren't dealing with just anybody. I had a lot of experience with this new level of incompetence. It worked.

"The doctor will be returning on the twenty-eighth, but I'm sure if there was something wrong we would have heard by now."

Kindness. Empathy. Strange emotions coming from this doctor's office. How did this assistant ever manage to get hired?

I accepted this as a small victory, since I had learned the specific date of the doctor's return and received a reassurance that nothing was wrong. And yet, I had an intuitive feeling that something was wrong. I decided to search for my rosary.

## 2/14/08: Biopsy Results

On Valentine's Day, at 8:40 p.m., the doctor called.

"Mr. Michaels?"

"Yes," I said, thinking, *Who else would answer my phone?* I lived alone.

"Dr. Hartless here."

"Yes." I realized my mouth was dry.

"We decided to stay another week."

*Who cares?* I thought. *I don't know if I'm going to die of cancer or anxiety, and he's telling me about his vacation.*

"Your biopsy results have come in. Do you have a minute?" and then there was a long pause. When your doctor asks you if you have a minute, you know you're in trouble.

"You have a Gleason score of (3 + 3 = 6) and a T2." Silence. Then I realized he expected me to respond.

"What does that mean?" I managed to get out. When scared shitless, I become very helpless.

"What about the 6 and the 3+3, and the T number?" Another long sigh. "Gleason scores help doctors determine how far the cancer has spread and its aggressiveness. The different numbers indicate how similar the biopsied cells are to normal prostate cells. Cells most like normal receive a two, those with the most deformity receive a ten. Your Gleason suggests Stage I cancer affecting less than five percent of the tissue and the T2 indicates a moderate aggressiveness." All I heard was that I had an aggressive form of cancer. I had blanked on the word "moderate."

"Yours is 3 + 3. The first number is the grade assigned to the cancer that is more numerous, and the second number, which is also 3, is the grade assigned to the cancer that is the second most numerous."

He might as well have been speaking Greek to me because I didn't understand a word he was saying.

"There is nothing saying that the cancer may or may not have spread out to the margins. That's the area outside of the prostate. Further testing or surgery would give you a more definitive answer."

All I could comprehend is that I had two cancers with scores of 3. *Two* that were *aggressive*. They could have *spread*. Two cancers that have spread and are aggressive. *I'll be dead in a month,* I thought. *Three, tops. Why didn't he just tell me that?* At this point, I was beyond anxious.

When you talk to your doctor, you will likely feel anxiety as well, and you may miss details. Ask the doctor if you can record office and phone conversations so you don't miss anything. Then when you are calm, you can review the information.

"What should I do next?" I asked.

"There are some options open to you."

Death was the only one that came to mind.

"If you decide to have your prostate removed, I can do the surgery. Just call the nurse to make the arrangements."

*Arrangements? Isn't that what you do for a funeral?* I thought.

"If you decide to have radiation or another procedure, I'll give you some referrals," he said, rattling off a familiar script.

"Thank you, Doctor," I said, since I had been taught to be polite. Especially to authority.

"You're welcome." *Click.*

*Happy Valentine's Day,* I thought. *Cancer loves me.*

## Processing

Even though I knew cancer was insidiously destroying my prostate gland and my sexuality, I decided to deal with it as calmly as possible and not let it affect my everyday activities, or so I thought. Instead, I wore less-than-fresh clothes to work, arrived consistently late, and snapped at my coworkers. I really didn't care about anything. I was angry and depressed, two sides of the same coin. I was angry my body had let me down and depressed because I had nowhere to direct my anger. I had always been healthy. Sure, colds, flu, a broken foot, but this was *cancer.* I knew I wasn't meant to live forever, but this wasn't fair. I even exercised.

The next day I began to research on the internet.

# 2. Internet Overload

## The Internet

When I began my search, a number of sites came up. Some were helpful and informative. Others illustrated hanging penises and hidden prostates. The majority had the same information:

1. The urethra leads to the prostate.
2. The prostate is a gland about the size of a walnut.
3. The purpose of the gland is to produce seminal fluid for semen.

Most sites were written in what I refer to as medicalese (diagnoses with long Latin words explaining more Latin diagnoses). I'm sure many of you have had a doctor talk to you using medical terms. After they're done, you feel like you were in a foreign-language class. I have learned to ask, "What does that mean?" Some doctors don't like it, but it usually works. I think they actually forget they are using Latin.

## Clinical Studies

Many sites dealt with clinical studies using rats. Although of some interest, there was always a qualifier at the end of the article along the lines of: "These studies have not been attempt-ed using human samples." Or "This could take at least another five years to be approved by the FDA." I question the FDA's role, since later results often overrode original findings. As a cancer survivor, I know the sense of urgency and feel cancer doesn't wait for approvals. I know there is *compassionate care*, which treats individuals whose cancer has resisted all other treatments. But isn't this a little late?

Reading about these studies only made me feel more frustrated. I needed something now. I didn't feel I could wait three to five years. I ruled out that avenue.

## Online Support Groups

Next, I discovered prostate cancer support groups. I was hopeful that reading about other men experiencing similar problems would help educate me about my own cancer. READERS BEWARE. Most of the time I would find a URL, get redirected, subscribe, and before I knew it, I was being asked to join a workshop and make a donation.

When I checked my desktop screen, it was filled with folders. Documents overflowed from each one, reflecting my state of mind.

I decided to take a break. I grabbed a can of cleanser and some scouring pads on my way to the bathroom. I shook green pellets across three tiles, wet a scouring pad, knelt, and scrubbed, determined to erase each spot and scuff until the floor was sparkling clean and up to my standards. During my recovery, I casually mentioned to Dr. Ego that my bathroom was spotless and how I managed to do it.

He tipped his head, held a pencil to his lips, and then pointed to me and said, "Obsessive, perhaps?"

"Perhaps. But ... but ... but ..."

"I'm sorry it's time to stop. We'll pick this up next week."

I did learn I was obsessive. But that seemed minor compared to cancer. I refused to give up hope, though, and continued my quest to find a group I would find useful.

## Chat Rooms

Chat rooms can be public or private. They allow you to discuss any issues you wish, but more often than not, they deal with sex. I was hoping to learn more about treatment options and others' experiences. User names often reflect personalities. Mine was SOS. In my first post, I said that I had just discovered I had prostate cancer and needed help. BNAROND welcomed me and wanted to know how many times I'd had my prostate massaged. I told him my experience had been very unpleasant. Even though he lived a hundred miles away, he offered to come by and give me a pleasant one. I politely declined. BEAMS tried to convince me to get photon treatment. This involved forty-four treatments in a private facility in the San Bernardino Mountains. Although intriguing, I was afraid I'd never be heard from again.

I decided chat rooms weren't for me.

## Forums

Forums involve people discussing a specific topic. In this case, it was prostatectomy, which involved the total removal of the prostate. NOT4GTN talked about not being able to get a full erection for the last three years. Since, at that time, I had no intention of having my prostate removed, I immediately dismissed his comments. But, eventually, I learned the art of "lurking." You could log on and read without detection. It seemed voyeuristic, but there wasn't any law against it. Still, I felt that I was committing some sort of sin.

METROTECH had had the da Vinci method, which is a robot-assisted prostatectomy. Although this had a science-fiction appeal, it still involved removal. I would not have some robot operating on my prostate. What if it misunderstood the command? What if the doctor manipulating the robot was hung over and couldn't see the nerve bundles or find my lymph nodes? What if the robot suddenly took on a life of its own and started removing other organs: heart, bladder, or kidney? (Of course, I had seen *I, Robot*, and I associated robots with mega-bad outcomes.) Rationally, I knew that robots are supposed to follow the most basic rules of the universe, and they are:

1. A robot may not injure a human being.
2. A robot must follow the command of the human.

But in my postdiagnostic state, it was hard to stay factual: too many negatives. Too many variables. Too many "alternative facts."

The forum proved to be overwhelming. I had read about too many methods from too many people, and everyone insisted that their procedure was the right one. It was all TMI (too much information). I shut down the computer and went to sleep.

(Spoiler: I finally did choose the da Vinci procedure.)

That night I had a dream, a dream of a chorus line singing and doing high kicks, like the Rockettes, but these weren't the

Rockettes. It was a chorus line of prostates with one woman in the middle. A familiar woman, Carol Channing. She stepped out of line, held out her hand, and said, "HELLO, KENNY. CAN I PUT YOUR PROSTATE IN OUR SHOW?" I woke up in a cold sweat. Only then did I realize I was having a nightmare. I decided I had to limit my time on the computer.

In spite of my best intentions not to log on, I was back at it the next day, searching for the "holy prostate site." I was as persistent as Sir Lancelot and as effective as Don Quixote.

In hindsight, I was anxious, frightened, and afraid I wouldn't find anything that would help me. I was operating from sheer desperation. I was at a stage where I was looking for an unobtainable magic bullet: a treatment that would be painless, eradicate my cancer, and increase my libido.

The truth was that I was still in denial. I knew I had cancer, but I was not looking at side effects such as impotence. "Impotence" is such a negative word. It implies that we, as men, will have no power, which is very different from not having an erection. Unfortunately, the word is used so often in prostate cancer discussions, it takes on a life of its own.

Impotence translates to:

1. I can't pretend to know the directions to every location without using GPS.
2. I will no longer be in charge of the remote control.
3. I will never win another argument.

The truth is our behavior will remain intact, and we will be as likable or dislikable as we always were.

But back to my internet search. The next day, I stumbled across a group called Us TOO, a support group that looked promising. Us TOO proved to be more than the right site. It led me to find a person who truly cared about me and was there for me 24/7. I sent an email to Roland, a member of the organization, telling him about the problems I was having deciding on the right procedure. Originally, I wanted to have radium seed implants, technically called brachytherapy. But after all my research, I didn't know what I should choose.

Roland not only responded to my email, he called me. He patiently addressed all my issues, from doctors to procedures to sex after prostate cancer. He even confided that he had had a penile implant, which made him King Kong of the bedroom. This device allowed him to control his erections by pressing a button implanted in his testes. Not only had I discovered the holy prostate site, I had found Roland, Erection King of the Prostate Round Table.

# 3. Between a Rock and a Hard Place

In hindsight, this period was filled with frustration and despair. There were times I felt like saying, "I'll stick with the cancer and take my chances." I'd quit my job, sell everything, and travel. It didn't seem like such a bad idea.

One of my relatives, an Auntie Mame type, had died of skin cancer at fifty-two, after refusing treatment. She lived her dreams, moving wherever she wanted, dragging her husband with her. She fled the Midwestern winters and enjoyed staying in a Mexican hacienda across the border. Then, she took off for Florida and stayed there a few years. My mother, diagnosed with lung cancer at seventy-six, opted for homeopathic treatment from an MD and lived to ninety. She saw her specialist regularly, watched her diet, and exercised.

We all know someone who has had cancer. Some have been treated for it, fought the battle, and won; others have lost. It is a very personal choice. One only you can make.

Quality of life verses a possible cure. I hear this all the time in the forums and groups. With prostate cancer, the key word here is "quality." Many men opt for surgery and then are bitter that they are impotent. It may be disappointing, but they are alive. Survivors may not have the life they anticipated, but this holds true regardless of being dealt the cancer card.

In my case, I wondered if I could handle possible impotence or incontinence. I learned that prostate cancer can be one of the slowest-growing cancers, and with active surveillance, I could postpone treatment for as long as five years or more. Just when I thought I had bought a little time, I also discovered that the longer I waited, the higher the chances were of its metastasizing to other organs and bones.

Choices are most often made after biopsy results. A Gleason score reveals rate of growth and stage of cancer. Some say if the cancer is contained and the Gleason low, you can do "watchful waiting," getting your PSA checked every three months. Others bury their heads in the sand and do "wishful waiting." Unfortunately, this is just another form of denial. A Gleason over six is considered serious and a surgeon generally recommends surgery. Mine was six, which only made my decision more difficult. I had cancer on the cusp, so to speak. I wanted to make an educated decision but was frightened and easily influenced.

When it comes to this decision, there is a lot of controversy as to what is the right choice. If you are young, meaning in your forties, fifties, or even sixties, you can choose active surveillance. But this isn't do nothing and wait. You don't have the surgery, but you choose different options. Some valuable tools to use if you decide on this approach:

PSA scores every six months
Biopsies that include the grade and cancer volume
Family history
Age of onset in family members
Baseline score early, despite protests of doctors
Enhanced doppler imaging with contrast
MRI

A recent study of 6,849 men in Sweden (Carlsson et al., 2014), with localized prostate cancer and under the age of seventy, concluded that surveillance may be a suitable treatment option for many patients with low-risk disease. This conclusion is controversial, since I believe that many men would use it as a reason not to do anything, and the cancer could then spread. On the other hand, the patient isn't affected by surgery or other treatments that can impact the quality of life.

Even though I knew active surveillance could have been an option for me, my anxiety increased to the point where my doctor prescribed an antidepressant, Wellbutrin, and a relaxant, Valium. After a few torturous weeks, I finally decided to take control of my own life. If I didn't, I felt I'd die of a heart attack or stroke rather than cancer. Since I am a worrier by nature, I knew I couldn't go on wondering whether the cancer was spreading or not. If my mother were around, I would've said, "Help me, I feel like a yo-yo, Ma."

I made the decision to have my surgery as soon as possible and scheduled it for April 9, 2008, at the Mayo Clinic. It was early March, and I decided to spend the month trying to have as much sexual contact as possible, even though we were under a blizzard bombardment.

# 4. Coming Out

In 2007, the year before, I had decided to attend a group for coming out. I was sixty-four and, like prostate cancer, had been in the closet far too long. It had been quite a time: my mother died the year before, and shortly after, I was diagnosed with prostate cancer. Add to that I was brought up to be a devout Catholic. Although I had not been a practicing Catholic for years, there was always that residual guilt, no matter how much I tried to avoid it.

I had experimented sexually during my teens and college years, which I chalked up to adolescent curiosity. I had come out of the closet so many times that the closet had become a revolving door. But after I met Lisa, I stopped and lived a straight life.

This was not unusual for men of my age group. In fact, many men had married, had kids, and continued to lead a double life, since homosexuality was not an accepted lifestyle during that time.

I lived with Lisa for twenty-two years; we had no children. I knew I was gay but was unable to tell her. Our relationship was monogamous and stayed that way until we broke up in 2004. After that, I started experimenting and sleeping with men, but I was still too terrified to come out. I think part of it was that I was afraid of what my parents would think about it and that I would be rejected. I believed my mother knew but hadn't wanted to talk about it. Now that they were dead, it didn't matter. I don't think it was logical, but I had been brought up to be homophobic, so it was a difficult conflict and did require individual therapy, which helped. I was in another place in my life now. I was ready to switch teams.

I joined a coming-out group at the Center on Halsted in Chicago and found I was not alone. Many men there were in similar situations. Some were still married and were struggling with their feelings and desires. I attended sixteen weeks of meetings and finally decided to tell my remaining family and my friends as well. When I told my sister, she refused to accept I was gay and told me I was really bisexual. I tried to convince her that I was gay, but she was insistent on keeping me in the bisexual category. Then I told my brother and his response was, "We all knew that. How's the weather there?"

I told friends and was surprised that most comments were like my brother's. No one really cared who I slept with. I felt like a huge burden had been lifted from my shoulders. With each revealing, I became stronger and less frightened to share my preference.

Some acquaintances asked if my ex-wife knew, and I told them that she didn't, but I wasn't really sure about that. We had not separated on good terms and weren't in touch with each other anymore. We'd had a long history, and I concentrated on remembering the good times and there had been a lot of them. I missed her, but I also knew it was time to move on.

# 5. Prostate Cancer's Reputation

I soon learned that people were less shocked about my sexual status than they were about my having prostate cancer. This may sound normal, but it wasn't. Women were more sympathetic and helpful than men. When I brought it up with other men, most didn't want to hear about it. Prostate cancer was still in the closet. Breast cancer was light-years ahead in being accepted and treated. Most women I knew had a yearly mammogram, which had proved to be a useful tool in detection. Most doctors were on board with recommending it.

At the time, the only known method for men was to have a blood test to determine a current PSA reading and baseline, along with a digital rectal exam (DRE). When I spoke to the men I knew, they didn't even know what PSAs and DREs were. I tried to explain and encourage my male friends to have this done. It was simple and could save their lives. Most tuned me out at this point. It was an uncomfortable subject and one that most men didn't want to discuss.

I believe most men avoid going to the doctor either out of fear or denial. Some of this is due to the macho stereotype, emulating the role of their family or culture. I learned that it was important to have a yearly physical early in life.

A large majority of men are also squeamish about certain procedures such as the digital rectal exam, even though it usually takes a minute or two. Early screening saved my life, but when I tried to discuss this with other men, they didn't want to talk about it. Through further research and discussions, I also discovered that a large percentage of black men are more vulnerable to prostate cancer due to many factors, including physiology and socioeconomics (Benson et al., 2006).

# 6. Prostate Cancer and African Americans

I know I had a tough time once my cancer was detected. I'm hoping my story helps all men experiencing prostate cancer, but research indicates African American men are 60 percent more likely to develop prostate cancer than Caucasians are. They're also twice as likely to die from it than any other group.

All men have what are known as androgen-receptor proteins—they are the receptors for the hormones that regulate male traits like facial hair and baldness. But researchers (Benson et al., 2006) have found that the levels of those proteins are 22 percent higher in the prostates of African Americans than in whites. And even more striking, they are 81 percent higher in the prostate cancers of African Americans.

Some studies indicate that black men may have increased enzyme activity, which may increase their risk of prostate cancer. Dr. James Mohler, Chair, Department of Urology, Professor of Oncology, Roswell Park Cancer Institute, is considered one of the top authorities on androgen studies in prostate cancer, and some of his research has been quite illuminating in this area.

Other studies indicate that many black men's prostate cancer is not detected until it is in its advanced stages. This may be due to lack of testing and detection. Regardless, knowing this, men in this demographic need to be more aware about their choices, since the disease can be detected, treated, and cured.

Malecare (a website that specializes in all aspects of men's cancer) makes the following observations:

> Prostate cancer is a leading killer of black men. Despite this, African Americans and black men worldwide are underrepresented in important medical research to find treatments and to help save their lives.
>
> Malecare's staff recommends that all men, upon attaining adulthood, discuss prostate cancer and the latest prostate cancer–screening tests with their physicians annually. Malecare has a two-prong strategy for ending prostate cancer disparities between African Americans and other groups.

According to Malecare's website:

1. Young men and Health program: Using popular blogs and podcasts, the website creates exciting connections with African American fathers and sons and demand for health care.

2. The website established its African American Prostate Cancer Research Center (AAPCRC) to "Increase African American access to health care. Create practitioner conferencing for research on African Americans and Prostate Cancer. Increase African American participation in clinical trials. Provide a comprehensive central repository of research on African Americans and Prostate Cancer."
   (www.malecare.org)

Collecting information can help a man make an informed and educated decision. Dealing with the diagnosis is difficult enough. Use the tools available to help make better choices. Knowledge is power.

# 7. Spare My Nerves

Although I had made my decision, I wasn't psychologically ready to have the operation. I had done my research and knew the basic procedures that were to be performed, but imagining and knowing are two different things. I knew it was essential for the surgeon to spare as many nerves as possible if I were to regain my ability to get and sustain an erection.

My research indicated that minuscule autonomic nerves surrounded the prostate. It was the surgeon's responsibility to separate them from the prostate before removing the organ. For me, that meant the surgeon must be patient and accurate.

There is a specific number of nerves, and they are usually referred to as group of tiny fibers, which together form a neurovascular bundle. Sparing these bundles is key to sexual recovery. Since the nerves surround the prostate, rather than lie adjacent to it, they are referred to as bilateral or unilateral.

If the surgeon is able to say that the bilateral nerves were spared, he is referring to nerves on both sides rather than one side (unilateral). The more nerves spared, generally, the better your chances of getting an erection. Drugs may be necessary after surgery, but the result is still an erection.

Since the prostate is often compared to the size of a walnut, the idea of preserving the nerves surrounding such a small organ seemed daunting. It can't be done well unless the area is magnified. With the advances in laparoscopic surgery, specifically the da Vinci, the area can be magnified a thousand times or more. The surgeon, who is robot assisted, can thus be more precise than he has ever been before.

The goal of surgery is to remove cancer. The surgical team won't know the extent and degree of cancer until the procedure is under way, so it is difficult for medical personnel to make specific promises as to outcome. This is important to know, since the surgeon will usually refrain from giving a yes or no answer to the question, "Will I be able to have sex again?" He doesn't want to give any false hopes. If the cancer has spread beyond the margins of the prostate, the doctor may have to remove the nerves completely in order to help ensure the best chances of survival. This lessens your odds of erections but increases your chances of living. I would rather have my doctor be as honest as possible before surgery than make excuses after. Dr. Kareful was honest, and I never felt as if I had been given vague promises.

The operation can last anywhere from two to eight hours, depending on the degree and extent of the cancer. Time becomes an elusive factor: if the operation was lengthy, did that mean the cancer had spread or did it mean the surgeon was trying to spare as many nerves as possible? Since I was under anesthesia, the question seemed moot anyway. My brother did tell me that the operation and time in recovery lasted six hours.

# 8. Another Perspective

I had mentioned earlier that there are a lot of perceptions regarding prostate cancer. I have been elaborating on my feelings and experiences from diagnosis through deciding on surgery, but I'd also like to share some comments I heard from others about their choices.

The da Vinci method was considered the new kid on the block when I had my prostatectomy. It's received a lot of press because of the results and short healing time. As time goes on, I think many more men will opt for this procedure. Fewer options were available when I began writing in 2008. There were only six da Vinci robots in the country, which certainly limited how many men could even receive the procedure.

To me, sexual functioning was important. I think most men tend to identify sexual abilities with being a man. I know I did. If I were unable to perform, it would affect me psychologically and could lead to severe depression. I am a psychotherapist and know how men feel about sexual performance or lack thereof. Men think about sex much more than women do, according to some studies, but in truth, it depends on the study and how the results are measured. According to (Fisher et al., 2011), men also think about sleep and food, and when the final results were in, the amount of time thinking about sex was smaller than thought, and the reporting depends on sex-role expectations. Yet, sexual conversations are quite rare in doctors' offices. I learned much more about all these issues from Roland, my Us TOO friend. He delved into my feelings during recovery and helped me explore my sense of feeling *what's the use?* He called and gave me pep talks. He told me I was on the right track. I would be *out of the woods* soon. He helped pull me through the worst of it. He was very candid and frank about sexual functioning, which was helpful to me as I confronted my own post-op concerns. Obviously, sex was still very much on his mind, and by choosing an implant, he'd found a way to make sure he could follow through.

I knew my sex life would never be the same after the operation. For one, I would never ejaculate. Many men share concerns about this. I hear it all the time in the forums. I had never thought much about ejaculating and I don't think men do, until they can't. Climaxing and feeling the semen erupt is part of the whole sexual experience. At least that's how I felt, but I couldn't do anything about that. I am lucky that I can still climax, and when I think of it that way, I can accept the tradeoff. It takes time to adjust, but I did. Being alive and cancer-free is the big win.

Some women who have had breast cancer talk about it quite openly with other women. Emotions are their verbal currency. Men would rather discuss sports any day than share emotions associated with prostate cancer. They deny the treatment has affected their marriage or family.

Men need to be aware that they will have to make adjustments. They should know that medication and other options are available to them. But men need to talk about their fears, their sense of sexual inadequacy, and other emotions they may be experiencing.

I feel strongly about this because as a psychotherapist and a survivor, I know it never helps to hold in those emotions.

Eventually, those feelings will manifest in another way, usually through anger or loss of control. This isn't necessary. If a man talks openly to someone—his partner or spouse, a friend, or another prostate cancer survivor—he will heal faster, both physically and emotionally. I feel so much work needs to be done in this area. It starts with the doctors. They need to be educated in talking about a patient's feelings. Let us know we will be bombarded by all types of feelings. Inform us that it is all right to seek help if we feel overwhelmed. Most important, encourage us to talk to someone.

Maybe surgeons feel they have finished their job once they have removed the prostate. Yes, they have removed the disease, but they have not touched the *cancer of the soul*. They have not treated the racing thoughts that keep us awake, the humiliation of incontinence, or the fear of impotence.

These are all transitions. All are part of healing, and I feel it is the doctor's responsibility to at least be aware of feelings. If you are a doctor, recognize these emotions exist. At least suggest that there are support groups out there that may help us. Give patients a group's phone number, brochure, or website information. Physical help is important but so is emotional health.

This is an area that the whole medical community needs to deal with if it expects patients to heal completely. For most patients, the physical component is just the beginning of the healing process. Men recovering from a prostate procedure and those who surround them are in desperate need of support. It's time to include emotional wellness as part of the whole man.

# 9. Robots Rule

I know I mentioned earlier that a robot would never operate on me. I was so conflicted about having the standard prostatectomy, where the surgeons remove the prostate unassisted, or the robot-aided da Vinci procedure. The night before the surgery, one of my surgeons called me and asked, "Which procedure did you decide on again?" I confirmed it was the da Vinci. "I just wanted to make sure, since you changed your mind a few times," he said. The surgeon was being polite. He didn't want to say that I was one of the most neurotic men he'd ever met.

The day of the operation, April 9, arrived, and I was to report to St. Mary's Hospital, a wing of Mayo's large complex. My brother, Pat, made the trip with me, and I was very glad to have him at my side. We entered the hospital lobby and I was surprised at the large crowd. It snaked around the entire room, doubled back, and started again. Surely, all these people were not there for surgery. How many rooms did they have? It was 5:45 a.m. I hadn't eaten or had my coffee, which meant I was one of the walking dead, and maybe this was a blessing. Did the rest of the room feel the same way?

I was given a wristband, making me an official patient, and sent to another line, which reminded me of the first time I registered for my college courses. It was in a large campus auditorium, where I was directed from one line to another, not knowing what I was doing.

Although there must have been hundreds assembled in hospital registration, I remember hearing conversations that seemed out of sync with the crowd, some loud and garrulous, others muted. But since I was decaffeinated, people could have been having normal conversations. I was definitely not myself, whatever that was. I made the rounds, confirming my identity and existence. I later thought this repetition was a form of imprinting to help my memory after surgery. A brain without food or caffeine is not a pretty state.

Next, I was downsized into a group of about thirty. Then we were divided again, into a group of six. I was feeling like a split atom. Finally, I heard my name called and knew this was it. I said goodbye to my brother.

"I'll—I'll be fine," I heard myself saying, reassuring my kid brother.

"See you on the other side," he replied.

"Of the hospital, right?"

Then we laughed, hugged, even cried. But just for a moment.

I followed the nurse down the hall as she explained pre-op procedures and then took my vitals. My Catholicism started to dominate my thinking, and I interpreted every result with a quote from the Bible, even though the verses were not completely correct. Somewhere I felt I was being punished because of my sinful life.

"Your weight is one hundred sixteen ..."

I heard, *"A fatted calf will be offered to God"* —but maybe He would overlook me since I was so skinny.

"Temp is ninety-eight point six, blood pressure, one twenty over seventy."

*"Many are called, but few are chosen." Lucky me*, I thought.

"A technician will take you to the operating room," the nurse explained, but that was not going to happen until I was finished with a few more unpleasant procedures, including an enema or two.

Much of it was a blur. What I do remember is that I was extremely frightened.

Survivors had recommended that I use this fear rather than let it overwhelm me. Treat it as a newly developed muscle. One you can control. Tense, relax, repeat. This practical form of creative visualization helped relax me and gave me a sense of peace for about five minutes.

Next was the dreaded enema, which only managed to make me feel more humiliated than I already felt. Of course, I had been asked to wear the ridiculous paper gown with unreachable back ties and the blue bonnet with an elastic band. Someone needs to rethink this outfit, regardless of how practical it is for the surgeons. Let us think we are going into surgery dressed well, even though it's all coming off. But then I reminded myself this was not a fashion show.

From here on, each step that brought me closer to surgery took on a whimsical quality, and I put myself into another world. I met the anesthesiologist next, Dr. Dreams, who reminded me of the Mad Hatter in *Alice's Adventures in Wonderland*. The relaxing tranquilizer had already been added to the solution dripping into my system.

"I'd love a spot of tea," I said.

"One lump or two?" the Mad Hatter asked.

"None, please. I don't care to vomit."

"Do not fear. I've attended the Queen nigh for many years," he reassured me.

I so wanted to be Alice, to take a drop of the potion and disappear into a rabbit hole. Obviously, the pre-op drugs had kicked in. Was I Alice in Mayoland?

Wait, a moment of lucidity.

"Hi, Ken. Dr. Kareful, here. Do you have any questions for me?"

So many. So little time. He was bending over the gurney and his surgical mask was already around his neck. All he had to do was pull it up and he'd be ready to manipulate the robot TO CUT OUT MY PROSTATE. DID I REALLY AGREE TO THIS?

Instead, I asked, "Are you a morning person?"

"Yes. And you are my first patient."

I heard, "Stick with me, kiddo. I'm your ticket out of here."

I took that as a good omen.

Perhaps HE was the Mad Hatter. He had helped Alice escape.

"I'd like to see the robot before the operation," I said.

"Of course. You'll see it when you get into the room."

I was excited. Being operated on by a robot. It certainly was better than being beheaded by the cruel Queen of Hearts.

When I saw it, I panicked. Granted, I have an overactive imagination, but there wasn't any resemblance to R2-D2. Nothing like the robots in *I, Robot*. What I saw was a monitor, other surgeons who reminded me of nuns wearing habits, and digital blinking lights.

"Is that it?" I asked.

Drugs. Too much? Too little? All I could think of was, *Too late.*

Dr. Dreams told me it was time for the countdown. "Ten, nine and three-quarters, nine and a half, nine and one-quarter." I was trying to stall.

"You will kill the dragon, good knight."

The next thing I heard was, "Mr. Michaels. Do you know where you are?"

"Heaven?" I ventured.

"No, you're in ..."

"Don't tell me. It's the other place."

"The recovery room."

*The recovery room*, I thought. Then I realized it was over. Filled with joy and song, I lifted my head and belted out:

*"Goodbye, cancer, my old friend.*

*Don't come back ever again."*

A number of patients applauded, but it may have all been a dream.

Regardless, I felt like I rocked Mayo Clinic. I was a recovering star. Rehab was next. I was definitely in the fast lane.

# 10. Toots Galore

After the operation, I cautiously checked my testicles and, with a great sigh of relief, saw that everything was still intact. Somewhere in my unconscious was the fear that I might be castrated. What then? Concubine to a sheik? Soprano in a boys' choir? But I was too old and couldn't carry a tune. These were not pleasant thoughts.

As I mentioned earlier, I was afraid the robot would malfunction, remove organs randomly, or implant foreign devices. Instead, the only thing I could detect was a six-foot blue-tube catheter that emptied into a plastic bag. My urethra, normally connected to the prostate, had been severed and was now connected only to my bladder. The catheter allowed the muscles and damaged nerves to heal.

I wondered if I had made the right choice, but it was too late to change my mind. I knew now that I had to accept my decision and move forward. Just as I realized my angst was getting the upper hand, Dr. Kareful came into my room. "How are you doing?"

"Good. Thanks."

"The cancer was contained to the prostate. And it had not spread to the margins."

This was great news. If the cancer had spread outside the margins, it could have metastasized to the lymph nodes and to other organs.

I was being given another chance at life and reminded myself not to waste it. After hearing the doctor's good news, I finally fell into a deep sleep, dreaming of a land filled with cupcakes, banana bread, and chocolate. But when I awoke, I knew I wouldn't get any of those unless I left the hospital. I assumed my release was contingent on having a bowel movement. Constipation runs in our family, so I knew I could be there for two weeks rather than the usual two days. I had started taking stool softeners prior to surgery, and the doctors had prescribed them twice daily following surgery. Nothing had changed.

I realized I had only one other option: *exercise.* I also prayed for a miracle and wondered which saint had been assigned this unpleasant task. In Catholicism, saints are associated with certain areas of expertise, depending on their miracles. Saint Francis, for instance, is the patron saint of animals. I thought of Saint Jude, the patron saint of lost causes, then remembered St. Moses, a less popular saint. He had not disappointed me before and I needed a miraculous intervention.

The problem with miracles is that they are unpredictable. They can take years, and, although I liked Mayo, I didn't want to become a fixture. The next morning, I forced myself to stand up and held on to my catheter. But I needed something for balance. During one of my visits to the chapel, I had noticed a portable pew, about three feet high and two feet wide. I decided God wouldn't mind if I borrowed it. It was for a good cause, and people can pray standing up just as well as kneeling. I said a few extra Hail Marys for insurance.

## The Visual

Small man, bent over in pain, tightly clutching a Foley in his left hand as if it were his mother's cherished rosary, while pushing a portable pew ahead of him with his right. Unfashionable, impossible-to-tie hospital gown hangs askew. When tired, he stops and kneels in the pew. (People think he's praying.) I looked like I was on a pilgrimage. It was a pilgrimage of sorts, one for release.

I walked for periods of twenty minutes, using the nurses' station as my marker. I must have flashed them every time I passed, since my gown never stayed closed. How are you supposed to fasten it with all those ties in the back? The truth is no one really cared. Besides, the nurses had seen thousands of butts. And I wouldn't let this stop me. I was on a mission. I was bound and determined to win the Walk for Movement Marathon.

Twenty-four hours had ticked by and nothing. I had clocked about three miles in the Mayo halls. Whenever I thought I felt anything gastric, I ran to the bathroom. But this proved futile. I'd spend so long in there, my brother often asked, "Are you okay?" I know he was concerned about my health, but this had nothing to do with the surgery.

The nurses were kind, efficient, and professional. In fact, this applied to all of the personnel I met at Mayo. For extra points, the facility was well staffed. If I needed something, someone responded to my call within minutes.

It was now Thursday afternoon, and I was starting to resign myself to staying the weekend. Worry didn't help my situation. The sphincter muscles must be relaxed. I was sure mine were in knots.

But I had other things to stress about. The nurses began teaching me the intricacies of the catheter bags. There were two: the *day bag,* a fancy, wrap-around-the-calf Velcro model, and the *standard night bag,* the throw-over-the-wastebasket type. I had to learn the specific procedures of emptying, changing, and closing each.

The hospital had sent me a DVD prior to surgery entitled *The Proper Care of Your Catheter After Surgery.* I hadn't watched it and was now paying for this negligence. I had to demonstrate the techniques before I could leave the hospital. More pressure.

I am not very coordinated by nature and came very close to flunking Catheter 101. Squeeze, pinch, squeeze. Or was it squeeze, squeeze, pinch? I did finally get it, but when a nurse asked for a demonstration, I'd "Fall to Pieces," just like Patsy Cline. I decided I had catheter dyslexia. I'd pinch too soon, release too late, and soon I'd have a wet slipper or, worse, a small puddle. Being physically unable to keep everything immaculate only added to my frustration.

Finally, I learned the basics of changing and cleaning. The word "discharge" can be very motivating. If emptying the bags was Catheter 101, cleaning the bags was Advanced Catheter. Each time I changed a bag, I had to sterilize it. This involved using a solution of one part vinegar to two parts water, swishing it a few minutes, and hanging it up to dry. This may not sound like much, but when you are doing it four times a day, it can become tedious.

Changing bags could take me as long as thirty minutes. Unacceptable by Mayo standards; they expected it to be done in less than five minutes. It was worse than a NASCAR pit stop. I say this lovingly, though, because the staff was super. Although my time improved, it was never close to five minutes, and I became agitated, which only led to more constipation.

I conferenced with my brother and he agreed to change our flights and extend his stay at the hotel. Although resigned to a longer stay, I continued my pew marathon. It was good exercise and I learned to like it. It also took up time. During one of my laps, I felt an unexpected penis pull. I also saw that there wasn't any liquid in the bag. *A complication*, I thought. *That's all I need. I'll be here through the summer.*

Kind nurse Rosemary saw I was about to have a meltdown. She rushed over and very gently said, "Mr. Michaels, your tubing is tangled up in your slipper. Let me help you."

NOTE TO SELF: *Always check water hoses before any trip.*

"Mr. Michaels, have you had any bowel activity?" Although I considered lying, I decided against it. It wasn't worth the guilt.

"Nothing major. Maybe a few"—I hesitated—"toots." (I had never used that word in my life, but my mother had. I was trying to be as respectful as the Mayo staff.)

"You passed gas?" she asked.

"Yes, but nothing after that," I mumbled, staring at the hospital tile, moving one foot from side to side.

"That's the greatest news I've heard all day." She smiled, clapped her hands, and gave me a high five.

My right hand reached out to hers, and I nearly lost my balance as I let go of my mobile pew. "Why?" I asked, furiously trying not to fall on my face.

"It means your system is working. Wait 'til I tell the other girls." She ran to the nurses' station, and before long, the staff encircled me.

One of the techs said, "This is what makes us excited in the urology department. Once your doctor hears that, you'll probably be discharged."

This was almost as exciting as hearing my cancer hadn't spread. Weird, right?

I kept thinking, *All I needed were toots.* And then I laughed. I laughed so loud, I tooted. I laughed until I cried. I had never used phrases like, "What a big toot. Whew, smell that toot."

My brother rushed into the hall, thinking I was crying, not laughing. When I was finally able to tell him what happened, he laughed, and then I *tooted.*

# 11. The Shutoff Valve

I was so glad to get home that I didn't care about having to wear a catheter. I was told not to drive, but I had to pick up my dog, Nathan. I had boarded him while I was gone, and I suppose I could have taken a cab, but it seemed like so much trouble. When Nathan saw me, he gave me pug kisses all over and sat close to me. Once home, we both took a long nap.

Safely in the house, it was easy to manage my bag. But if I was out during the day, it was difficult to know if the leg bag was full. I'd have to find a restroom to check it. If it was, I'd put my foot on the toilet rim, open the valve, and empty it with one big *whoosh. How cool,* I thought. The bag just filled up and then I emptied it. It wasn't something I wanted to do forever, but I could handle it. But the sense of being "Joe Cool" vanished quickly. It became a complete nuisance. I slept a lot during those days. In fact, I was completely exhausted. Some days I would get up, have breakfast, go back to sleep until lunch, eat, and return to bed.

I did have to walk Nathan twice a day. Occasionally, I'd watch TV for a few hours and then sleep the rest of the night. There weren't any rules. Who was there to say I shouldn't? I wouldn't have listened anyway because my body needed sleep.

I didn't have any appetite, though, which was a bad sign for me. It was not unusual for me to stop eating when I was stressed, but the operation was over, I was back home with my dog, and I couldn't understand why I'd worry. I was taking codeine for pain and that may have been the reason. My friend Lynne had stocked my refrigerator with food and desserts of all kinds. I had a lot to choose from, when and if I was hungry. Sometimes a meal might be a container of rice pudding topped with whipped cream or a pint of French vanilla ice cream or a piece of Key lime pie. And so it went. This phase of recovery lasted two weeks, and then I was scheduled to return to Mayo to have my catheter removed.

Eventually, I began to eat more, but certain routine functions, like showering, became a real chore, especially with the catheter. I didn't know where to hang it when I showered, since the tubing was always in the way. I felt like a foreign device had been implanted in my penis. If this was some alien scheme to collect information, they certainly picked the wrong organ.

Eventually, I dreaded anything associated with the bag. The morning and evening rituals of changing and cleaning became loathsome. Even though I was more practiced, it could still take close to half an hour. Granted, I didn't have a heavy schedule, but this was not a chore I'd wish on anyone.

Wearing a bag did make me realize how much I took for granted. For me, it was only temporary, and I was thankful. I felt sorry for anyone who had to wear it longer or forever.

Once the catheter was removed, I had to deal with a new set of problems. The Mayo nurses had stressed the importance of proper hygiene. Otherwise, I risked infection and a longer recuperation.

This made me think of my Catholic schooling and how I had to follow their rules or suffer the consequences. Each nun had her own code and if you broke it, your fate was in her hands. They even made surprise visits to the boys' restroom, to make sure you weren't talking.

Consequently, I felt if I broke any rule, I was in very deep trouble. I didn't realize that this indoctrination could lead to problems down the road. For example:

**MAYO RULE #1:** Wash your hands with hot, soapy water to ensure cleanliness.

(Sister Theresa's Rule: Spend two minutes every time you wash your hands or your soul gets three months in purgatory.) I became obsessive about washing my hands.

**MAYO RULE #2:** Use a solution of one part vinegar, two parts water to sterilize the bags.

(Sister Eileen's Rule: Each week, one student will mop the classroom. Remember to use only one-third cup of soap. Any variation jeopardizes your soul to six months in purgatory.) To this day I measure my soap when cleaning.

**MAYO RULE #3:** Apply antibacterial cream to your penis to avoid chafing.

(Sister Caesarea's Rule: Touching your private parts other than for urination is a mortal sin. You'll catch leprosy and then go to hell.) I no longer worry about catching leprosy. Some rules are meant to be broken even though there is a twinge of guilt.

Once a Catholic, always a Catholic.

But I soon realized all I had was my catheter routine. I wasn't working because I couldn't. I wasn't socializing because

I wasn't in the mood. I wasn't visiting family because they were six hundred miles away.

At one point, I knew I was going stir-crazy and had to do something. I was no longer on codeine, so I was legally allowed to drive. I decided to do something simple, like go to the pet store. The store wasn't far from my house, and I thought I'd pick up a few goodies for my dog. I showered, shaved, got dressed, attached my leg bag, and was on my way.

I arrived at the store and began to meander through the aisles, searching. I knew I wouldn't walk out of there without spending at least fifty dollars, even though I had only planned on buying him a few treats. As I continued to walk down the aisles, I felt something strange on my leg. I knew I was wearing the leg bag, but this felt different. I couldn't quite put my finger on it. It seemed a lot of the other shoppers' dogs wanted to sniff me. Could they tell I was wearing a leg bag? That was ridiculous. How would they know? It was under my pants, as safe as wearing Harry Potter's invisible cape.

When I shop, I often return to previous aisles to make sure I haven't missed any clearance items. When I got to the toy aisle, I saw a narrow, wet trail that led to the spot where I'd stood before. *How odd*, I thought. It looked as if a dog had been following and tracking me.

Another dog came up to me and sniffed until his owner pulled him away. I went to the treat aisle again. I looked down and noticed a large puddle close to where I had been standing. I thought, *There are hand wipes in every aisle. You'd think owners would clean up their pets' accidents.* It was then that I thought to take a covert look at my leg bag. I lifted my pant leg and realized I had not turned the shutoff valve completely.

Much like Hansel and Gretel, I had left a trail. No wonder I had so many animal admirers. With that realization also came the fear of embarrassment. Had any owners seen this? How many knew why their dogs loved me so much?

Now I was leaking in the hamster aisle and they were spinning their wheels faster. I dropped all my purchases and bolted for the door.

I heard a clerk call, "Sir, sir!"

I pretended not to hear him. I was afraid I'd be asked to do cleanup or be given a lecture about potty habits. Worse, I'd be arrested for "indecent trailing." I made a dash for my car, leaving another trail, but the clerk was fast and closing in on me. I was busted. I reached for my keys. Couldn't find them. The clerk was next to me. Cornered. *No place to hide. No place to run.*

"It was the Chihuahua," I mumbled. "Didn't you see what he was doing?" *He can't talk. He's small. Let him take the rap.*

"No, sir. It's not the Chihuahua," he said.

It was a stupid excuse. I knew it was time to *fess up.*

"I'm sorry. I've never done anything like that before."

"Don't worry. People do it all the time."

*They do?* I thought to myself. "That's disgusting," I said.

"It's part of our job. When you left your items, you dropped your keys. I figured it was you."

Shock ... embarrassment ... freedom ... *Priceless.*

He had been referring to the items I had left in the hamster aisle, not the trails throughout the store. I raced home to change clothes. I never made that mistake with my day bag again and, for obvious reasons, never returned to that pet store either.

# 12. More Mayo, Please

Waiting to have my catheter removed seemed endless, even though it was only two weeks. Dealing with the bags became so repetitious, I felt like Bill Murray in *Groundhog Day,* an endless loop. I even thought of only wearing the night bag to make my life easier, but I couldn't bear staying in the house. Besides, I couldn't walk my dog using the night bag, which seemed to fill up within five minutes. I began crossing off days on the calendar, but this seemed to intensify the wait. I accepted my fate and said to myself, *This too shall pass.*

The pungent smell of white vinegar, usually a favorite salad-dressing ingredient of mine, now became Superhero Sanitizer. I was going to ask the nurses if there was a substitute but that was before they gave me a "goodies" bag containing a thirty-two-ounce bottle of vinegar, some extra tubing, and a directions pamphlet. What I would have done for a Snickers bar. But none of that mattered because I was alive. I had survived the operation and all of my demons and the good news was ... Well, I wasn't sure I had the good news.

But I will always be indebted to the staff and doctors of Mayo and respect them highly.

# 13. Are We Done Yet?

I made my plane reservations to return to Mayo. It took only fifty minutes to fly there as opposed to six hours of driving. I decided to stay at an older hotel known for its character, and it had plenty—small rooms, tiny elevators, odd food. Could I possibly be claustrophobic? By the time I settled in, it was eight p.m. and most places were closed. I could have had room service, but I needed a walk and some fresh air.

I crossed the street into a courtyard dominated by a defunct movie theater, which was now a museum. A vintage poster was displayed: James Dean, starring in *Rebel Without a Cause*. I wondered how he would have dealt with prostate cancer.

I entered the mall and was met by boisterous shouts of drinking college students and the glare of bright lights. It was filled with life. I looked into one restaurant, but there was a twenty-minute wait and my leg bag was running on full. Besides, the noise was a bit too much.

After spending a quiet, solitary life with my dog in my condo, I felt as if I had arrived at New York's Grand Central, overwhelmed and lost. I decided to forgo eating that night.

The excursion hadn't been a total loss, though. I had discovered a LensCrafters, which I planned to explore the next day to enjoy one of my favorite activities: recreational shopping. But here's an odd twist. I am so ambivalent about my choices that I either exchange or return what I've bought, and then stop buying for long periods of time. Shopping distracted me now. Reason? It kept me from negative thinking, since cancer seemed to be on my mind all the time.

NOTE TO YOU: *Find something to take your mind off your cancer.*

My Mayo appointment was at eleven a.m. in the Gonda building. I thought I could get there blindfolded, but I got lost. I barely arrived at the appointed time, another sign of my anxiety, since I am usually compulsively early.

"Mr. Michaels?" a tech called out, scanning the waiting room.

"Over here," I said, as I turned, bumped into another person, and then dropped my paperback.

If I hadn't been so nervous, it would have been comical. But I felt detached and scattered, much like a Dalí painting.

"Good morning. My name is Jim and I'll be your tech today."

"Hi. My name is Ken, but you know that already. Any specials today?"

"Step in here. Remove everything but your underpants. Slip on a gown. When you're ready, come back into the hallway. We'll be serving catheter removal with a side of diapers."

I smiled and shook my head in acknowledgment, wondering if I should keep my socks on. The floor was cold, and they had not provided those weird gray socks, one size fits no one. I decided to keep mine on, since this procedure had nothing to do with my feet. I stepped out in my argyles and stood there holding my Foley.

Jim ushered me into another room. "Mr. Michaels, I want you to get up on the table, lie on your right side, and slip off your shorts. Then we can get started."

I wondered why he hadn't told me to take off my shorts in the dressing room. After my previous experiences, I'd known those briefs were coming off sooner or later.

"I will be taking a look at your catheter and removing it."

*Alleluia*, I thought, perhaps a bit too soon.

He informed me of the procedure step-by-step. I appreciated his thoroughness.

"All right."

He gently touched and gripped the catheter. "This is going to hurt a bit. Then it will be over."

I have learned that "hurt a bit" is short for "excruciating pain." He twisted the catheter and pulled it out quickly.

*"Eeeah! Hooyee! Aaak!"* I screamed out.

Those weren't the words I used, but you get the idea.

"You all right? Can I get you some water?"

"Yes and yes."

And then came the joy of knowing the catheter was out. I had a flood of thoughts.

WILLIE was free, and it felt so good to be free. One of the best feelings I'd had in a long time ... it's all relative. (I call my penis Willie. You, of course, can call him whatever you wish. Your penis, I mean, not my penis. You have to name your own penis.)

"I have to take a few X-rays and show them to the doctor. Turn to your right. Deep breath. Don't move." The X-ray machine made a *cheesh* sound.

"Good, now turn to your left. Hold your breath. Don't Move." *Cheesh.* "One more and we're done." He left the room, telling me to relax. Like that was going to happen.

Thoughts going through my mind.

I still have cancer. The bladder connection didn't heal.

I had a tumor.

*Sure. Relax.*

"We need to take one more. The right one is a bit blurry, and we want to make sure all the X-rays are perfect." He had brought another technician with him, who was studying the X-ray and giving instructions.

*Something IS wrong*, I thought. *Cheesh.* Huddling. Whispers. Silence.

"Looks good. We'll show them to Dr. Gallonder and find out what she thinks. I hadn't met or heard about Dr. Gallonder. The idea that Dr. Gallonder was a female urologist at Mayo was a surprise and a sign that times had changed. When I attended college in the sixties, few women were enrolled in medical school.

A few terrifying minutes later, Jim returned and calmly proclaimed, "The doctor says everything looks great. You can get dressed now."

"That's it?"

"You'll talk to Dr. Kareful later today, and he'll go over everything in detail." I knew he was dodging answering the BIG question: Was there any indication of the "Big C"? I would wait, though. I knew it was useless to press Jim for more information. *That is the doctor's responsibility* would be the stock answer.

"You can put your briefs back on. I'm going to give you some diapers, and when you're ready, I'll show you how to use them. You'll be wearing either the infants' or the toddlers'. Try the infants' first."

I noticed that they were decorated with a superhero. Did that hero wear these to give him special powers? The only superpower I wished I had at this point was controlling my urination.

I weigh 116 pounds on a good day. I knew I was small, but infants' or toddlers'? What was he thinking? I wasn't sure what to do. I tried to put on the toddlers' diaper but couldn't get it around my waist. In fact, I couldn't get it to fit around my leg. Finally, completely exasperated, I walked out into the hall and said, "I can't get this diaper to fit. Am I doing something wrong?"

To his credit, he didn't laugh.

"You're supposed to lay them in the middle of your briefs."

I was past feeling stupid or embarrassed. I had been trying to wear the diaper as if it was the most natural thing to do.

"Oh. That would make things much easier." I went back in, put the diaper in my briefs, and walked out for another inspection.

"That's right. Now put on these polyester shorts. [These looked like shortened pantyhose.] And you'll be all set."

*For what*, I thought, *Mardi Gras*? They fit. I was done. It was noon, and I was to report back at 12:45 p.m. Of course I wasn't hungry. I decided to take a walk and enjoy the feeling of not wearing a catheter.

"Mr. Michaels, we'd like you to drink at least four glasses of water, and after you've urinated, please report back here. This test is to ensure everything is working properly."

On my first visit, they tested my flow rate. This time all they wanted was a flow. I drank four glasses of water and waited. Finally, I felt an urge, or so I thought. I went to the men's room and tried to urinate. Six drops dribbled out. Now I was supposed to report my output to the nurse.

"I only managed to get out a few drops," I said sadly.

"But urine did come out?" she asked encouragingly.

"Yes, it did."

"Was it a steady flow?"

"No, just a few drops."

"It sounds like it's working. I'll make a note for the doctor. You'll be seeing him next."

*I'm almost done,* I thought. *Two out of three. Only one more to go.*

Ten minutes later, I was seated in Dr. Kareful's office.

"Mr. Michaels, the X-rays look good," he said, smiling and shaking my hand. "Your bladder is working, although I see you were only able to dribble a little."

*This wasn't a basketball game,* I thought.

"It was all I could get out," I said.

"It looks good."

"Is the cancer gone?"

"We can't say for sure, but according to the X-rays, everything looks fine."

I was so overjoyed, I didn't know whether to hug him or bow. We settled for a strong handshake.

"Thank you, Doctor. You're the best."

"I'll want to see you in three months for a checkup and a PSA test. We wait three months because we feel everything has settled into place by then."

"Of course, of course. Is that it?"

"Yes. You're free to go."

*You're free to go.* Little did he know the power of those four little words. I went back to my room, packed my bag, and was gone. As the plane took off, I thought how lucky I was. *No complications, no catheter, and, most important, no sign of cancer, although the doctor hadn't said I was completely cancer-free.* Nevertheless, I'd take it and decided this was one of the happiest moments of my life.

# 14. Blitzing

When I arrived in Chicago, I decided to take the train home, since I didn't live that far from the airport and I didn't feel any need to rush. Besides, it saved me cab fare.

I unpacked and changed into jeans and a sweatshirt before I felt any urges. I saw my night catheter and tubing in the bathroom and decided I would destroy them in some ritualistic fashion, yet to be determined.

It had been over five hours since my flow test. I had had a Coke on the plane, and I still didn't need to go. I was checking my mail when I felt the first urge. *Good,* I thought. *Everything's going to be fine.*

All I had to do was aim at the toilet. It would be great to have control again, since it had been over two weeks. As I waited, I felt the stream coming and it was then that I *blitzed.* You probably haven't heard the word used in the way I employ it. The urine erupted from my pipeline and it didn't go in the toilet. It was so intense and strong that every urologist would have agreed my flow was off the charts. Off the charts and unleashed. I blitzed in every direction but the bowl; hitting the mirror, walls, and ceiling like a hose that had slipped out of a fireman's hands. All those glasses of water needed to be released. NOW.

There was urine everywhere. Even Nathan, who had come to check on me, got spritzed. The stream had hit everything except the toilet. Had something gone wrong? Had the doctors attached the wrong tube to my bladder? Had something become detached? I immediately called Mayo. I needed to know what was happening.

An attending took my call. “How can I help you, Mr. Michaels?”

“Something is terribly wrong. I tried to pee, and it didn’t go in the bowl. The stream, well, it wasn’t actually a stream. It was more like a flood. Actually, it was more like a blitzami.” I could see the headline: BLITZ DESTROYS EVERYTHING IT TOUCHES, LEAVING THOUSANDS DROWNED IN ITS WAKE.

“When did you have your catheter removed?” he asked calmly. They must have made a note that I tended to hyperbolize.

“About six hours ago.”

“And did you have a flow test?”

“Yes, but there was only a small dribble,” I apologized.

“You have nothing to worry about.”

“Nothing to worry ... I’ll probably have to file a flood report. I’m not sure my insurance will cover this. Can I get a note from you?” I felt like I was six years old.

“You have not used your urinary muscles for the last two weeks. They’re still healing. That’s why you wore the catheter.”

“Does Mayo provide insurance for this?”

He ignored my questions. At the time, I thought they made perfect sense.

“To allow the urine to flow into the Foley.”

“How long will this continue?” I asked.

“We don’t know.”

“Someone must know. I can’t keep doing this.”

"It all depends on you."

"Me? I can't control this."

"You were told about the Kegel exercises, weren't you?"

He was being very kind, but I was upset. I felt like a sixty-four-year-old child who not only wet his pants but had also hosed down the whole bathroom.

"Mr. Michaels, are you there?"

"Yes, yes. The Kegel exercises. They help strengthen my muscles—"

"That control your stream of urine. They've been weakened. Once you start doing your exercises, your normal flow will return."

"How long will that take?" I asked.

"It depends on the individual."

I knew that. I was feeling testy and desperately needed a shower.

"A week, two, three. A month?" He paused. "I've seen some people take as long as three months," he added.

"Three months?"

"I'm not saying it will take that long. You should regain it in time."

I wondered what would happen if I went to a public rest-room or out to dinner. I'd probably be arrested. I could already see myself in front of Judge Judy:

*"Did you or did you not urinate on these men in the rest-room?"*

*"It was out of my control. You can call my doctor at Mayo."*

*"I am not going to call your doctor. I repeat, Did you or did you not urinate on these men? Please answer the question."*

*"I did."*

*"Judgment is for the plaintiffs in the amount of 3,533 dollars for new suits, shoes, and pain and suffering."*

I was brought back to reality by the attending asking, "Mr. Michaels, are you still there?"

"Yes, I am, barely, but yes."

"Didn't we give you a few diapers?" the doctor asked.

"Yes, you did," I responded.

"How many?" he asked.

"Six," I said.

"If I were you, I'd buy a larger supply, just in case ..."

I knew then that I would need a lot more. "Thank you for your help, Doctor."

"You're welcome, and if you have any other questions, don't hesitate to call," he responded.

I wasn't sorry I called. The good news was that my plumbing was working. The bad news was the thought of prolonged incontinence.

This is where I regressed to being a toddler. My mother told me I potty trained early, so I was probably out of diapers when I was eighteen months. You never know when you'll need those skills again. This wasn't like taking a basic college course, which was often soon forgotten. This was a basic life skill that I needed to relearn.

I now know incontinence is common after prostate surgery, but I wish I had been warned. I never yearned to have my catheter back, but I sure hoped those muscles would regain functioning soon. I began to worry each time I took a whiz.

*Once you start doing your exercises, your normal flow will return,* replayed in my brain.

I wondered if accelerating my Kegel exercises would speed up the process. I searched for my Mayo literature, thinking there had to be a brochure or DVD somewhere. I finally found a pamphlet entitled *What to Expect After Your Catheter Is Removed* and read the article as fast as I could. There it was in black and white. *It is very common for men who have had a radical prostatectomy* ... skim, skim, skim. *The Kegel exercises help regain control* ... skim, skim, skim ... *as a set of six exercises, once a day. Be sure to be in a prone position ... Overtiring the muscles could make the situation worse.*

*Worse?* I certainly didn't need "worse." The muscles needed to heal slowly. I resigned myself to the fact I would have to take this ONE DAY AT A TIME and hoped that my muscles were strong and resilient. I wondered if there was a Kegels Anonymous in case I *slipped*?

It was near bedtime and I decided I better go one more time, not knowing what might happen once I fell asleep. I slowly aimed at the toilet bowl, stretching as far as I could, hoping to get closer to the bowl. This time I only blitzed the mirror in front of me. I cleaned the mirror and went to bed, feeling very depressed. But then I remembered another helpful AA phrase: "Progress, not perfection." How true. This time it was confined to one part of my bathroom. Besides, every man knows a penis has a mind of its own. I thought that only referred to sex. Mine had transgressed boundaries.

## 15. Diaper Depot

The next morning proved to be much of the same. I realized that if I didn't want any accidents, I could sit on the toilet, but this wouldn't help me regain control of my muscles. I made a conscious decision to conquer incontinence, too. This should have been simple compared to having the surgery. After all, I had sacrificed my prostate to stop my cancer. The truth is it's all relative. Each step has its own set of problems and challenges, but I was determined to win this battle, too.

I went to my local pharmacy and started looking through the diaper section. Do you know how many different kinds there are? They filled one whole aisle. Jumbo diapers with extra padding for preschool children, even special-occasion diapers. I couldn't see myself wearing moose diapers to meet the president of the local Rotary club. There were diapers for crawlers, eight to sixteen months. Nowhere did I see blitzers, fifty and up. I didn't want to go up to the counter and ask the clerk about what type of diaper he might recommend for someone like me. This was more embarrassing than the first time I had to buy condoms, a fantasy that took years to fulfill.

I still worried about what people thought. This time I imagined what the other people in the drugstore might be thinking: *Do you think he's shopping for his grandchildren? ... If he needs them, why doesn't he buy adult briefs?* Instead of worrying about lubed or not, I was concerned about padded or not. I did take a look at the briefs, which were obviously aimed at older adults; the label didn't explain anything other than the fact that they were diapers for incontinence. There, I said it: *I was afraid of being incontinent for the rest of my life.* At a critical sexual moment, I'd have to ask to be excused so I could take my ED medication and change my diaper. Isn't that romantic?

When I was ready to check out with a package of toddlers' padded jumbo diapers, I tried to camouflage what I was buying, but that's difficult to do when the package is that big. There were three people in line behind me when the cashier asked, "Did you find everything you were looking for?"

"I need diapers because of prostate surgery." A Kodak moment I wanted to delete. I was embarrassed again and sweating now. Yes, people were staring, not because I was incontinent but because I had stopped the line. The cashier paused her scanning, looked at me, and asked, "You have your ExtraCare card with you?"

"I didn't know diapers required extra care. I thought they were disposable."

"Sir, I don't care what you do with those diapers. The total comes to eight dollars and twenty-one cents. Will that be cash or charge?"

I pulled out my wallet and was so nervous, I dropped it on the counter. Then I couldn't find my debit card, and when I did, I couldn't get it out of my wallet. There were now seven people looking at me, wondering why I was holding up the line. I gave her a dollar and said, "Keep the change." Her expression stopped me dead cold. I pulled out a twenty.

I finally completed the purchase and ran for the door, except it was the entrance and wouldn't open. I faced an existential crisis: No Exit.

I was pounding on the door. Finally, a manager came over. "Sir, that's the entrance. The exit is over here." I rushed out. I needed to get some air, or was it a Xanax? I had been so nervous that I had some leakage. I didn't know if the diaper I was wearing had worked or if my pee had soaked through.

When I got home, I checked. The front of the diaper had folded back and I had wet myself. Luckily, my shorts had caught the overflow, and I was so glad to be wearing the Captain Underpants briefs from Mayo. I changed and tried the new jumbos. Luckily they worked, even though I felt I had a blanket in my shorts. I never felt at ease during this time. I'm sure no man does. You never know if your flood wall will malfunction, twist, or shift. It's humiliating and disconcerting.

I finally discovered diapers that had adhesive wings on the sides, which I hoped would make me feel more secure. Although a great concept, they didn't work. I resorted to duct tape to fasten the wings on my legs. Unfortunately for me, even this became undone. The diaper would stick to my legs, but then it pulled away and slid down to an area that left me unprotected. When I felt an urge to go, I would try to pull everything up front and hope it would catch the leakage before I got to the bathroom. This didn't always work. If I was wearing jeans, I usually didn't have enough time to get to the bathroom before my bladder decided we were close enough.

I'm not sure if I started to heal or the exercises began to work, but after about three weeks, I had fewer accidents, although I usually had at least one a day. If I was lucky, it was only minor. There were a couple of nights of bed-wetting. I let the first one slide because I thought it was my fault for drinking too much water. The second time, I was on the phone to Mayo the next morning. I thought this one was on them.

"Is this the urology department?"

"Yes."

"This is Mr. Michaels. Do you remember me?"

"Yes."

"I've had a few bed-wetting incidents."

I went on to describe them in detail, as I have a habit of doing, and ended by asking, "Do you think I need to buy a rubber mat or a tarp?"

"Neither. It's perfectly normal. You have nothing to worry about."

"Are you sure?"

"Yes. If it happens again, give us a call."

Thankfully, it happened only twice. Another example of my tendency to worry.

When I went out, my first stop would be the closest restroom, where I'd try to urinate and then adjust anything that had moved. I knew if I laughed, coughed, or sneezed, I had leakage. If I stood up too quickly, I had leakage. If I got too nervous about anything, I had leakage. You can see the dilemma I was in. Leakage became associated with everything I did.

I found it difficult to balance expeditions with home time. There came a point where shopping at Target became a luxury. I'd push the envelope and stay out an extra five minutes because I *was a wild and crazy kind of guy*. I'd even given up watching *Jeopardy!* so I could spend a little extra time grocery shopping.

One of my most hated chores is doing laundry. I have memories of schlepping loads of clothes to Laundromats for years.

Consequently, I owned at least thirty pair of underwear. But even this didn't seem like enough when I was going through three pair a day. I stocked up and now had a closet of underwear that covered the spectrum as far as color and type.

During this time, I spoke to another prostate cancer survivor, and he shared his method for keeping the leakage in check. He wore liners, a super-jumbo diaper, two pair of cotton briefs, and one rubber pair. I didn't want to go through the nuisance of buying rubber briefs, but I did own a pair of bicycle shorts. I tried this once and found I couldn't button my pants. For everything to fit, I had to wear my sweats. I looked like I had gained twenty pounds, and when it was time to go, it took so long to get to the real deal, the outcome was inevitable. I tried this only once.

As time went on, I finally transitioned to liners. Buying those made my experience with diapers seem simple. (Since my diaper-shopping days, I have learned that the most absorbent kind are those used for neonatal infants; consider this if you need to use diapers during your recovery.)

# 16. Silver Linings

*Recovery is a journey*
*One I'd rather not repeat*
*Endurance is the key.*
—MY POST-OP MANTRA

I went to a different drugstore, since I felt too embarrassed to return to the one where I had experienced the diaper fiasco. After pretending to browse for ten minutes, I found the liners in the feminine hygiene section. There were two aisles devoted to products I had never even known existed. I had to consider length, absorption, and thickness. For example, there was super-thin, extra-absorbent and extra-long, or average. Many women picked up whatever they needed, gave me a strange stare, and quickly moved on. I decided I wasn't going to go through the agonizing guesswork that I had gone through with diapers. I picked up two products and marched up to the pharmacy counter. My experiences of surgery, catheter, and leakage had helped me develop some courage. A twentysomething Asian man was filling scripts. I walked to his counter and said, "I've had a prostatectomy, and I'm having leakage problems. Could you tell me which of these products would be best?"

There was a long silence, and he blushed, stuttering, "I-I don't know, sir. I'll get someone else to help you." Too young to have any idea of what to advise. The next pharmacist was a thin woman, early thirties, no makeup, who reminded me of Sister Cecelia. My heart rate began to climb to a dangerous level, since this nun had abused us so badly, a few kids had to see a doctor. In those days, our parents felt we had it coming. The thought of asking a nunlike figure such a question triggered a panic attack, and I felt myself beginning to hyperventilate. And here I thought I had been doing so well.

To my surprise, she gave me a timid smile and asked, “How can I help you?”

Her name badge identified her as Nancy, and she was trying to be very attentive. Each time I finished explaining a part of my situation, she would nod in understanding. Once I was done, I realized I was becoming more disjointed and awkward. I heard myself say, “I switched to winged super-absorbent, but they kept overlapping. I knew this was TMI. She didn’t need to know why some liners didn’t quite work. But she never gave me that *I’m pretending to listen, but I’ve tuned you out* look. I hoped she wasn’t thinking of calling security.

I finished with a sincere, “I could use your help.”

Her eyes acknowledged that she understood. She hadn’t been condescending or shocked—and she wasn’t one of my former nuns. She rose to the occasion.

“I don’t think you need the super-absorbent guards unless you are having excessive leakage.”

“No, it’s just occasional at this point.”

“It would also depend on how many you were using each day,” she said with what I believed was actual concern.

“I was only using one a day by the end of my diaper stage.”

“Then, I would get the normal absorbency in our generic brand since it’s cheaper.”

“Okay.”

"I don't recommend the winged guards because sometimes the wings adhere to the legs, which can cause irritation."

"Oh, I know. I had some terrible irritation around my inner thighs from the tape."

A male customer had arrived and was standing behind me as the pharmacist and I discussed the pros and cons of panty guards. When he realized what we were discussing, he immediately went to the other side of the pharmacy and asked for his prescription. I was so relieved to have someone actually help me that I ignored his look of disgust.

*This woman is doing her best to assist me*, I thought.

"Any other questions?"

*Would you marry me?* crossed my mind. Nancy was nice, supportive. Granted, I was gay, but she was kind. Not only had she understood, but she even offered to put away the super-absorbency liners. What more did I need?

Once the guards were in a bag, I felt I had accomplished my goal. When I got home, I tore open the package and realized each pad was wrapped like a little Christmas present. I ripped through the packaging like a little child opening a new gift, hoping for something special. There it was, a long pad, narrow in the middle and wider and rounder at the ends.

"Thank you, Santa. I've always wanted these."

I tried one on. They were much less bulky than the diapers and a perfect fit. It took me three days to realize the paper on the other side needed to be removed, and that I was wearing them backward. I wondered if Nancy was working. There was adhesive under the paper, which would stick to my briefs. Maybe I could call her tomorrow. No more duct tape that ripped my skin off every time I pulled off the pad. Who'd designed such a wonderful product? Shouldn't I be shopping for a ring? I looked for a name or a manufacturer. I would send a thank-you card for the brilliant design. It took a while for me to realize the liners weren't custom designed for me. Women had been using these for years. There were a few prostate survivors who knew their value, but we were the minority. After a couple of days, I wanted to share this discovery with every man who was experiencing post-op leakage. I was grateful to my friend who had suggested the combination of panty guards and an extra pair of briefs. It took so little to make me happy then. I thought of Nancy. *She's probably married ... and don't forget, you're on a different team.*

During this period, I began to feel more confident about being in public. If by chance I did have leakage, I didn't worry it would break through my protective layers, since the flow was much lighter. Using the bathroom proved to be a challenge, though, because of the layers. I soon discovered that the best way of handling it was to push my penis to the side and squeeze it through the layers. This proved to be somewhat difficult in the beginning, but I soon got the hang of it. I took pride in these small accomplishments because they were all-consuming.

Adult briefs might have made my life a lot easier, and I'm sure they're a good product. Unfortunately, I associated them with illness and infirmity. And I surely didn't fall into either category. In my mind, adult briefs not only meant incontinence, they meant death. I know that doesn't make much sense, but that was my reasoning. I rationalized it by saying they were more expensive and disposable. After all, it was just for a short time. Isn't that what my doctor told me? Actually, he didn't.

*"Time varies."*

*"Approximately?"* I asked.

*"I wish I could tell you."*

It was true. No one could predict how long the incontinence would last.

*"Some men never regain control."*

I decided that was not an option.

# 17. Shrink, Shrank, Shrunk

Presurgery, I had spent a great deal of time researching prostate surgery, options, and consequences. I felt I had done my homework. The side effects of all that information, including depression, were overwhelming. In fact, I'm sure I repressed the information about *penis shrinkage.*

Of course, none of the doctors mentioned this to me either before or after the operation. Since this circumstance deals much more with psychological than physical issues, it may fall into that gray area of what's discussed/not discussed in the doctor's office. I'd like to think my doctor was being protective and was trying not to make me feel even more worried than I was, since prostate cancer's side effects so often revolve around sexual concerns and performance.

Once the prostrate is removed, the urethra must be stretched and attached to the bladder, which is generally quite pliant and adjusts. This stretch and pull may cause the penis to look smaller after surgery. According to Dr. John Mulhall, director of the Male Sexual and Reproductive Medicine Program at Memorial Sloan Kettering Cancer Center in New York, most men will experience some penile length loss after surgery, and that is permanent. Occasionally, that will improve, but if there is documented loss after six months, it most likely will not improve after twelve months (Seaman 2017).

Many of you may think, *What's the big deal? A little shrinkage. So what*? But I don't think men want to hear about possible incontinence, impotence, and *shrinkage*. Each man is different regarding size, but I don't think any man wants to hear he's going to have less.

And we come to the age-old question, *Does size matter?* The average male penis is between five to seven inches long. Some men who are well endowed may be as large as nine or ten inches. The assumption is that penis size is proportionate to the height and weight of the person, but this does not always hold true. The fact is, it is genetic. My feeling is that, as shallow as it may sound, size does matter. Not only to men, but also to women, whether they admit it or not. This is based on conversation and observations and is not statistically documented, but I've had a lot of discussions. Men who are larger seem to be endowed with confidence. They claim to be *more of a man.* Whether size affects performance is questionable. It certainly has no bearing on procreation or number of children a couple decides to have.

In discussions I have had with women, most prefer a man's competence in the bedroom, regardless of his penis size, though. They do say it's a bonus if he's large, but if he's not skilled and considerate, they feel they will get little satisfaction. Ultimately, fulfillment is the goal.

Perception may depend on education and enlightenment. I do think most partners would choose communication and intimacy over size. Ideally, these qualities are interconnected and provide a fulfilling relationship.

# 18. The Kegel Workout

Mastering Kegel exercises would be an important part of my recuperation, including, I hoped, the gradual end to my incontinence. Most doctors and other patients agreed that it was important to begin Kegels before surgery because it would make the pelvic muscles stronger. I had never heard of these exercises before, so I was intrigued to learn about what they were, how to do them, and what they achieved.

According to the Mayo Clinic website, "Kegel exercises for men can help improve bladder control and possibly improve sexual performance." The article goes on to say that Kegels can help strengthen pelvic floor muscles after a prostatectomy. It states the benefits and explains how to do the exercises, recommending they become part of a daily health regime for best results.

I started my Kegels before surgery, hoping I was doing them right. Directions often instruct you to sit on the toilet, isolate your sphincter muscles, and then move on to the muscles above them—the pelvic floor muscles. I found it difficult to locate the exact area at first, but in time, it does get easier.

I tried the Kegel toilet technique, but I found I didn't like spending a lot of time doing exercises in the bathroom. The truth is you can do Kegels anywhere: while waiting for a red light to change, at your desk, watching TV. I soon discovered every person had a different approach and that there were many types of Kegels. Since I enjoyed working out, I liked learning a new set of exercises. Also helpful in my post-op recovery was that I could do Kegels stretched out in an easy, relaxed pose.

There was the basic Kegel, not to be confused with basic cable, although it was the bare minimum. It's done prone or sitting with your feet on the floor, isolating the muscles, then squeezing them for a count of ten. Pause for sixty seconds and then do another set of ten. I was told to do six sets every night before going to sleep, since I would already be prone in bed.

Since Kegels really aren't very exciting on their own, I eventually developed a mantra for my reps:

*BAGEL, BAGEL,*
*CRUNCH THAT KEGEL.*
*LET'S GO KEGEL!*

When I was healed enough to return to the gym, I tried not to chant this too loud. I would lie on a mat and pretend to stretch. No one can actually detect Kegel activity.

After more research, I learned there were other Kegel exercises, such as the quick pump, the hold and release, and the elevator. These specific Kegel exercises are meant for those who have mastered the basic Kegel. The quick pump involves pulsing the Kegel much like any targeted muscle. The hold and release is self-explanatory, and the elevator involves holding the Kegel at different strengths, mild to intense. This could be quite a workout, and I began to fantasize about a Kegel gym for prostate post-op rehabbers. Among the classes:

*KEGEL INTRODUCTORY*: Demonstration and practice using the basic *search and squeeze*. This would be to learn where to localize.

> *KEGEL MEDITATION*: Finding the *inner you* through Kegels. You could chant while doing Kegels. You could get in touch with your *inner self*, while *being one* with your Kegels, thus releasing stress.

> *KEGEL POWER*: Using barbells and weights while doing each type of Kegel. This would provide focus and strength while building muscles in other areas of your body.

Once established, I could market DVDs, T-shirts, and entice movie stars to be spokesmen ... Some fantasy, right?

Since I was confused by all the different Kegels and wondered if I was ready for the power plan, I contacted Mayo. Their advice was the standard: "Stick to the six sets per day. Don't overdo them and don't overtire. Otherwise, you run the risk of more leakage and possible total incontinence." Although my enthusiasm was diminished, I was determined to revolutionize the Kegel model and to be the Kegel Champion of the World. But one step at a time.

# 19. Dreaded Digital

We know from experience that the proper maintenance of a vehicle, a house, or any major appliance can help extend its optimum performance. The same thing applies to our bodies. I learned the importance of good health after spending a great deal of time in San Francisco, where residents put a high priority on health. There, I began getting yearly physicals, which I continue to this day. I went to the same doctor every year, and we usually went through the same routine annually, like clockwork. When you're young, you don't worry about illness, and in most cases, why should you? Your body is at its peak, and generally nothing goes wrong, but I do think there should be more emphasis on exercise and diet. My generation was brought up at a time when playing outdoors was what we did, and for the most part, it served us well.

Another observation is that, in general, women are more health conscious. They tend to live longer because they take better care of themselves and are more aware of their emotions. Getting a yearly mammogram has become routine for most women over forty, and, consequently, early breast cancer detection is up. They know that early detection can save their lives. This exam can be painful, I hear, and yet women don't let that stop them from having one. Mammograms aren't perfect, but along with knowing family history, they can be key to successfully detecting and treating breast cancer.

Men need to start doing the same thing. We have been socialized to believe that we can endure and work through pain. If we don't talk about a problem, it will disappear. I will openly admit that I don't like to see a doctor, and friends, usually female, will press me to go if a problem continues. Sound familiar? Often, we end up in the emergency room because of our stubbornness. I think this all relates to the idea of being masculine, a *macho kind of guy*. We are still in the Stone Age. We work and play harder. Being the provider and breadwinner isn't as popular as it once was, but the standard still exists in some societies.

The reason I bring this up is that I think most men fear going to a doctor unless they must. One of the reasons I believe many men avoid checkups is due to the dreaded digital rectal exam, also known as the DRE. Every man who has ever gone for a physical knows what I'm referring to. After checking all the vital organs, the physician usually says, "And now I'm going to check your prostate." This simple exam involves the doctor inserting his finger (digit) into your rectum and palpating the prostate to check for unusual swelling or growths, which can be an indicator of disease. Usually, your physician will order a PSA test as part of your blood work. If it hasn't been included, you should ask for one. The test determines how many antigens your prostate is producing. A low score (1–3) generally indicates a healthy prostate, and a high score (6 and up), the opposite. I'm not going to go into specifics about this, but it is important to know your score. Using it as a baseline and being aware of it for future physicals is as important as knowing your blood pressure.

Another reason men may fear getting a DRE is because some are still homophobic. It's time to overcome this because it is unfounded. The doctor is doing his job, and giving a DRE is part of it. I'm sure it is not something he looks forward to, but he does it. The test is short. Let the doctor do his job.

And you should do yours. Ask questions, get answers, and know your numbers.

Being aware and catching cancer early may save your life. I know it did mine.

It has also saved the lives of many men, some of them very prominent. Ben Stiller told a *Today* anchor that he's "really fortunate" to call himself "cancer-free." Stiller said prostate cancer "wasn't on my radar at all" before he started taking the PSA tests, which he attributes to saving his life.

# 20. Viva Viagra

Post-op, I wanted to know when I could resume sexual activity. My doctor suggested eight weeks, but I heard others say anywhere from six to seven.

I think I was really asking, "Will I *be able* to have sex? Ultimately, will I be able to get an erection?" There are so many variables involved: amount of nerve damage, finesse and skill of the surgeon, degree of cancer, and, likely the most important factor, fear. The male ego is a wondrous and fragile creature. When a man feels sexually fit, he can endure poverty, disaster, and trauma. But suggest vulnerability or unreliability, and sex may never occur.

After surgery, most urologists prescribe one of the PDE5 inhibitors. These aid in the body's production of nitric oxide, which relaxes the muscles and allows more blood to flow to the corpus cavernosum—the tissue that makes a penis hard during sex. Together, PDE5 inhibitors and sexual stimulation usually lead to an erection.

Dr. Kareful recommended a small dose of Viagra, and I took it religiously. Other drugs in this group are Cialis and Levitra. Most people associate these with erectile dysfunction (ED), and although that is their primary function, Viagra (sildenafil) was originally discovered as a drug to treat angina. Care must be exercised when taking these drugs, though; they're not appropriate for all men. There is some risk involved, especially if a man is already taking nitrates for heart problems. Be sure to consult with your physician.

Even with ED drugs, it may be a while before you're able to have an erection. Remember, you are a postprocedure patient, and it will take time before bruised tissue and ego heal. Researchers state that it may take men who have had prostatectomies as long as two years before they can get and maintain an erection good enough for intercourse (Dererr, D., 2006).

I was sixty-four at the time of my prostatectomy. Post-op there were physical factors I had to face that were related more to aging than to surgery. In my younger days, getting an erection was simple. When I got into my sixties, I sometimes depended on my ED drugs, as needed. Sex was a large part of my life, whether fantasized or real. I didn't have an adolescent's libido, but I didn't have one foot in the grave either. Let's just say, I was *active* and wanted to stay that way. When I heard that I might not get an erection for a year post-op, and possibly never, I only became more determined to prove *everyone* wrong.

I think medical staff were trying to tell me that intimacy, not sex, was still an option for me. You'd think as a psychotherapist I would have known that, but denial is a powerful coping mechanism. That lesson was one I carried back with me when I resumed being a therapist. Repetition and patience are essential during psychological treatment.

After my hospital stay I returned to Chicago, and my friends Lynne and Jim insisted I stay with them. Their care was the kind only true friends can provide. In fact, I felt as if I had been transferred to a Mayo annex. They left me alone when necessary but were there when I needed them. Solicitous but gracious.

During my early days of recovery, I went through some very depressing times. Looking back, I refer to them as the Dark Days of Cancer, and they were some of the worst days of my life.

For those of you familiar with Harry Potter, I felt like I was being devoured by the Death Eaters, whose goal is to take your soul and deprive you of any feelings of hope. When that happened, I didn't want to get out of bed, eat, or shower. I didn't care what I did. I was constantly afraid that the cancer would return. I was convinced I'd never have sex again. I didn't have the energy to reach out to friends, and when I thought about it, having a conversation seemed all consuming. I'd try to watch TV but stared at it blankly.

My dog would cuddle in my lap, trying to give me some comfort, and I didn't even notice him. I lost my appetite and any sense of hope. I felt the only person who would understand was my mom, and then I'd realize she was gone, which would only make me more depressed. Yes, I was feeling sorry for myself.

I was also grieving—for my lost prostate and everything it represented. I didn't care that the cancer had been caught in time. *In time for what?* I thought to myself. There wasn't anything that could make me feel better. I allowed myself to slide down that slippery slope, knowing there was only more darkness at the bottom.

These periods could last one or two days or as long as a week. I'm sure other cancer patients have experienced these feelings, but that didn't give me any solace. I felt truly alone.

Even on my best days, I believe that humans feel isolated. Although we may be surrounded by family and friends, ultimately we have only ourselves. This thought made me feel depressed at times as I coped with recovering from my cancer surgery and its effects. I truly felt alone. This may sound existential, but it's what I thought. I still do, even though I'm feeling better.

Finally, I reached out to my cousin Chris, who had been diagnosed with non-Hodgkin's lymphoma. If anyone could understand what I was going through, it would be him. He assured me that what I was experiencing was completely natural.

"Chris, I feel so negative."

"It's okay."

"It's not healthy."

"I've gone through it many times."

"But I don't care if I die."

"It will pass."

"I'm not so sure."

"I've gone through it. It does."

I decided to believe him, and it was a good decision. Being able to say what I felt allowed me to *move on.* I'm not sure what would have happened had it not been for Chris. He was my guardian angel, like Clarence in *It's a Wonderful Life.*

My advice to anyone going through a serious health challenge is to try to reach out to someone: a partner, a family member, a counselor. These are days you get through somehow, but having somebody to talk to can really help.

When I started to recover, I wondered how I did it. The fact that I did empowered me. It made me realize how precious life is and how important it is to live it. Try to remember that, especially when you start to feel better. Enjoy every minute as if it is your last. We've all heard that, and yet we still get caught up in the minutiae of everyday living. That's normal, but the more aware we are of death, the more we can enjoy life.

Eventually, my dark period passed, and I found myself caring about getting an erection, this time not from insecurity, but from the desire to return to intimacy. I knew I was healthy and allowed myself to embrace these feelings. I was obviously starting to feel better and getting back on the road to life. At times I wondered if this tentative libido had any basis or if it was just imagined. In one of my graduate classes, I had been taught that amputees sensed feelings in phantom limbs. I hoped I wouldn't have a phantom erection.

As my eighth week of recovery grew near, I began to count the days. I felt a sexual New Year approaching, one filled with surprises. I began to experiment and felt a mild response; I hoped against a false sense of anticipation. My tentative touches led to more daring moves.

My nascent Catholicism woke up and chimed in, and Sister Caesarea's warning played in my thoughts repeatedly: "Any indecent touching is a mortal sin and will be gravely punished." Despite this, I continued. I was tempting spiritual damnation, but basic instincts had taken over.

And then it happened. Eureka, an erection. There was no stopping me now.

I continued to enjoy a sense of pleasure and, finally, I ejaculated. I thought it was a miracle because I was told I might climax but never ejaculate semen again.

But on further examination, I realized I had ejaculated urine. I didn't know whether to be disgusted or elated. Finally,

I decided something was better than nothing—the plumbing worked and that's what was important.

Other survivors had said they had been happy with these results. They said it was different but good. I began to realize what they meant. Obviously, the nerve bundles were functioning. I didn't want to analyze it too much. I wanted to enjoy and savor this moment, which I did.

I needed to feel upbeat after surgery, blitzing, and diapers. But it is critical to move through post-op one step at a time. This is key. Every person's recovery is unique. What is universal to all is trying to stay hopeful and positive and taking it one day at a time.

Find a doctor who is helpful, not discouraging. Reach out for support. Was I lucky? Maybe. But I also believe I was informed and determined to get the best treatment I could. This took time and research, but it paid off. Try not to panic. Do your homework. Then you can join me in saying, "Viva Viagra!"

## A Special Note to Gay Readers

If you are gay and prefer anal sex, it is strongly recommended you wait at least eight weeks to avoid irreparable damage to the tissues in that area. When in doubt, ask your MD. If the doctor doesn't have answers, start researching. There are gay support groups out there.

# 21. Vacuums, Pumps, and Implants

Although I was able to have an orgasm, I wanted even more. I was searching for a magical solution that would allow me to have sex like I had before the operation. This was impossible, but I wasn't ready to accept that yet.

The search for sexual wellness is a big business, one that promises to address any problem or fantasy you may have. My guess is websites about sexual satisfaction are among the most popular on the internet.

## Vacuums

These are endorsed by other patients, but I had never used one. The vacuum's function is to bring blood to the penis and trap it there with an elastic ring, which will lead to an erection. It's important to know that if the ring is kept on longer than the suggested time, the penis can be permanently damaged.

There are all types: plastic, glass, hand pumped, and the ultimate, automatic model, which requires only an electrical outlet. Some pumps actually place the ring on the penis, which eliminates any manual fumbling. These rings come in a variety of sizes, colors, and materials (plastic, steel, elastic). Vacuums range anywhere from $30 to $200, depending on the model you choose. Some may be sold at your local pharmacy and don't require a prescription.

Some postsurgery literature recommended the vacuum as a tool to be used along with Viagra. It probably had some psychological value, since the visual could be self-affirming. *Use it or lose it* was the guiding principle here. I thought of ordering one, but it was nonreturnable, which was enough reason for me not to buy it. Since my doctor didn't feel I needed one, I didn't pursue it.

## Injections

These have to be prescribed by a urologist who specializes in post-op prostate patients. Dosing involves self-injecting the head or side of the penis. I knew this meant pain, and this was something I wanted to avoid if I could.

I have since learned that many men do inject. Although the prescribed drugs may vary, the shots basically work the same way. Drugs that open the arteries are injected directly into the penis. As a result, blood flows in and an erection should result.

Some injected drugs are also available as a gel, which is absorbed by the penis. Injections and gels are prepared at a pharmacy. Each is mixed according to the amount your doctor prescribes, and this often varies from individual to individual. You should see an expert urologist, one who is familiar with these ED treatments and is able to adjust your dosage according to your results (McHargue, 2017). The injections are expensive: $200 to $300 each. But the advantage is an erection that may last up to an hour.

## Pumps

These are similar to vacuums but are sleeves that fit over the penis and allow you to pump air around it, causing an erection. You still have to use an elastic ring to keep the erection.

## Extenders

There are items guaranteed to increase penis size, which is something to consider if you think your penis has shrunk drastically post-op. However, I feel these devices play on men's insecurities.

Extenders involve bands, wires, and straps: an apparatus that wraps around your penis and testicles. You are required to wear this four to six hours a day for at least two months. It looks like a torture device from the Spanish Inquisition.

I ruled this out immediately. I didn't want anything that painful-looking near my penis.

## Implants

These are considered the gold standard for guaranteeing an erection, and they require surgery. A plastic bulb is inserted in your scrotum and tubes are placed along the sides of your penis. Basically, the implant is designed so that a constant erection results, which can be manipulated. You can make sure your penis is facing down, so your erection isn't conspicuous.

Once you are ready for sex, you push your penis up and press on the scrotum as many times as needed to create the perfect erection. This erection lasts as long as you want, and when you are done, you tap your scrotum again and your penis returns to its normal erect state, which you push down. It is considered very effective.

I watched a video of the entire procedure and decided I wasn't ready to take this step. Also, I wasn't very "technically inclined," and with my luck, I would be inflating when I should be deflating, and I didn't need any more complications in my life. Besides, who knew what lay ahead in the future of implants? I decided to wait.

Although I did decide to hold off on drastic changes, I was glad I researched these options, because I wasn't sure what would happen if I stopped taking Viagra. There was little rationale for all this research, but during the time, I was not rational. Was I ever rational? Then again, what is rational?

# 22. Man's Best Friend

In November 2005, I adopted a black pug from a rescue in Michigan. His name was Nathan, and I decided to keep it that way. I had wanted a dog for several years, but I was working so much, I didn't think I had the time to take care of one.

My friend Lynne kept saying, "I think you need a dog." She owned a beagle named Snoopy, and I always enjoyed him. I told her all the reasons I thought I shouldn't get a dog, and, as most best friends do, she pointed out that none of the reasons held up when scrutinized. I finally relented and rearranged my work schedule. At the time, I was working twenty hours a week for Children's Hospital and was still maintaining my private practice as a psychotherapist, seeing patients in two different locations. I was able to negotiate my time at Children's, and I could arrange my own schedule with my patients.

Before I could say "fetch," I was a proud owner of Nathan the pug. He was large by breed standards, weighing twenty-eight pounds and standing ten inches tall. Most pugs are half that size. Later, I decided a roving bulldog had visited his pug mother, and I wondered how the rest of the litter turned out. Pugs come in different colors, but Nate was all black except for a white triangle on his chest. He was four years old, microchipped, and house-trained. Pugs are lovable, loyal, and comical. Since Nate was a rescue, I didn't know much about his past. I was able to learn that his owner, who sounds like she may have bred dogs for profit, had turned him over to the rescue because she thought he was aggressive. The rescue believed this and kept him isolated at first. Then they slowly introduced him to one other dog at a time to socialize him. It was then they learned that Nathan was actually a bit shy, but once he warmed up, he was playful and energetic.

He came into my life when my mother was quite ill. In the span of three years, she had suffered a broken hip and pelvis and a stroke. We didn't know it at the time, but she also had brain cancer. She didn't display any symptoms and luckily was lucid until the end.

On weekends, I often commuted from Chicago to Clinton Township, a suburb of Detroit. The trip was generally a six-hour drive. Nate accompanied me and became a great companion. It didn't take long for him to become part of the family. He often provided joy and humor for all of us at a time when it was difficult to find either.

My grandparents had been farming immigrants and consequently, my mother didn't see dogs as pets. She had been brought up on a farm, and Nate was just another animal. Before long, though, he won over even her heart. During one very difficult visit, we were all in a glum mood. Nate disappeared for a while, then returned to the living room and dropped a present at my feet: my sister's leopard-skin-patterned bra, which he had found in her bedroom!

My mother died on March 7, 2007. Nearly a year later, I was diagnosed with prostate cancer. As Gilda Radner said, "It's always something."

I was quite devastated by my mom's death, and although it was inevitable, I had a difficult time accepting it. I don't think anyone can accurately describe the loss of a mother. Whether I cried myself to sleep or waited to exhale, Nate was always there for me with unconditional love.

He continued to be my buddy through cancer treatment and recovery as only a dog can be. When I picked him up after my surgery, Nate sensed, as I believe most dogs do, that I was in pain both physically and emotionally, and he wouldn't leave my side. He was not accustomed to my being home all the time, and I'm sure he also enjoyed that—one small silver lining about my recovery time.

I had to walk Nate twice a day, and this helped because it forced me to go outside no matter how I felt. When I napped on the couch, he would make sure he was next to me, letting me know I was not alone. I often played with him when I was healthy, but he held off while I was recuperating. I think he felt his job was to take care of me. He was constantly under my feet wherever I went, though, and I had to watch that I didn't land in the hospital again, this time with a broken ankle.

Sometimes, for no reason at all, Nate would come over and start giving me his pug kisses. It was his way of showing me he was there for me. There is no question in my mind that pets are therapeutic, no matter what stage of life you're in.

When I had recovered enough to return to work, he went back to his routine. Nate kept me on my toes and often provided laughs and companionship. I still wonder what I would have done without him. Lynne had been so right. I had been ready for a dog. Little did I know, he would help me get through prostate cancer.

# 23. Dealing with Feelings

I had not seen my psychiatrist, Dr. Ego, since my surgery. The thought of talking about my experience and current feelings seemed overwhelming. Yet, he was the one who had been right about my having cancer in the first place. He encouraged me to see a urologist after my first PSA test. Then he supported my getting a biopsy, and once we knew the results, he had recommended Mayo Clinic.

I had avoided seeing Dr. Ego because I was in emotional pain and didn't want to deal with it. Yes, it was time to talk to him, even though I was resisting it.

During our session, I discussed the operation and its aftermath, my depression, and my sexual fears.

"And then I ejaculated urine."

"Great. That means the pipes are working. And you got an erection. Even climaxed. Do you know how long it takes some guys?"

"I know. I know. You're right."

He was always able to point out the positive and make me feel better. You may be thinking you don't need a shrink to figure that out, but I did. The only other people I had confided in were my brother, Pat, and my cousin, Chris.

This was an example of how difficult it was for me to talk about prostate cancer, even with my psychiatrist, especially about my sexual functioning. Luckily, I was comfortable enough to open up to my family and Dr. Ego. I'm sure this is something widely discussed in recovery groups, but I hadn't been able to go to one yet. It had taken me nearly two months to make an appointment with my shrink, which made me realize how reluctant I was to talk about my feelings. If I felt this way, I was sure there were many other prostate cancer patients who felt the same.

"Would you like to make another appointment?" my shrink asked.

"Not yet."

"Okay, call me when you're ready."

I was still resisting, and I wasn't sure why. But at least I had taken the first step. Looking back, I wasn't ready to process all my feelings about the experience. I knew that once I started seeing Dr. Ego weekly, I would have to deal with everything. It was all too raw.

You might think, *Well, isn't that the best time to see your shrink?*

*Yes*. But when it comes to therapy, not everything is logical. There is always a reason behind a thought or an action—even one that may not be apparent to the patient, and that included me. I think I was still angry at Dr. Ego for pointing me toward the test that ultimately yielded my cancer diagnosis. He was the harbinger of bad news. I was also ashamed that I was not the same man who saw him before the operation. There wasn't any reason to feel that, but I felt it, and I wasn't ready to deal with those feelings yet. Eventually I did come to terms with who I was post-op, but it all took time.

When I think about the resistance I had to making the appointment and talking about my recovery, I realize how loaded the subject was. By that, I mean it triggered all my sexual issues regarding performance, acceptance, and shame. Each one of these was complicated, and I knew I didn't have anyone else I could discuss them with. Although it was uncomfortable for me to open up, once I did, it was helpful, and I wondered why there weren't more groups for this sort of support. It was emotionally painful to have lost my prostate to cancer, but it was even worse to have to deal with getting back into sexual functioning. I realize that it triggered a primal chord in my unconscious. So deep, I didn't want to get close to it.

I eventually did and realized there was much about my illness that I couldn't control. I didn't ask for temporary incontinence and impotence. They were the result of my cancer and surgery. I was attempting to be constructive, not destructive. Occasionally, I still have problems with performance and inadequacy and try to be aware of their origins. It doesn't always work.

My outcome was on the positive end of the spectrum, and I feel the advice I got from Mayo was helpful. I know many men struggle with even more difficult outcomes—the cancer's spreading or losing all nerve bundles, to name just two. What if injections or other ED treatments didn't provide the results they expected? As far as I know, most men don't deal with these emotions. These thoughts stay buried and are not discussed with other men. Having sex even without the complications of cancer can be occasionally daunting. Having it after prostate surgery can be close to impossible at times.

Whenever I dealt with a patient who was going through a bout of temporary impotence, I stressed the importance of relaxation. I would tell him to avoid trying to perform. It was important to deal with intimacy, to deal with accepting and giving love, rather than the *act* of love. Generally, this helped.

My first post-op appointment with Dr. Ego wasn't the best session I ever had, but it was enough to make me feel that I wasn't alone and I should take pride in my progress. This was all I needed at that point in my recovery.

With more sessions, I resolved some of my issues, and I can only encourage anyone reading this to seek help. Try to uncover the issues that stop you from reaching your optimal performance. Some are physical. If that is your case, identify it, talk about it, and learn to accept it. If you don't have access to a counselor or therapist, look for survivor groups or ED specialists in your area. If that's too uncomfortable, try to link in to some of the resources I list at the end of my book.

There is life without sex, a different life, but one that can be satisfying and fulfilling. Don't spend the rest of your life beating yourself up for something you can't control.

# 24. Us TOO for You

Seeing my psychiatrist gave me strength to reach out. I realized I had been talking back to the TV and having conversations with my dog. It was time for me to get back out into the world and start socializing. I had met my mentor, Roland, through Us TOO. When he checked on me after surgery, he recommended the support group, which included prostate cancer patients and caretakers. Us TOO covers a wide area of issues, including initial diagnosis, intimacy, and recovery from surgery. I did some research. I found out that a local chapter was having a meeting at a hospital less than a mile from me, and it was scheduled for ten the next morning.

I was anxious about going and wasn't sure what to expect. It's my usual thing, social anxiety. I was afraid of being disliked and speaking in public, too, and I worried about saying the right thing. I often forgot that I had been an actor and performed in front of hundreds and had given workshops to professionals for years, which ultimately allowed me to overcome my fears.

As far as my physical recovery, I was still wearing a few liners, and I tried to avoid coffee and excess liquids to prevent any embarrassing situations.

I had arrived at the hospital at 9:50. I am compulsively early and usually bring along a book to help pass the time. I inquired at reception and was directed to the security area to get my visitor's pass. The skinny red-haired woman, who looked tougher than the security guard stationed in the lobby, was in charge.

"Hi. I'm here for the cancer group."

"Which cancer group?"

"Us TOO."

"Bless you."

"Us TOO."

"Sounds like you're coming down with a cold."

We stared at each other, and finally I said, "Prostate cancer."

"Sure it's not the lung?"

"I was sure until you brought it up. Who knows? It may have spread."

She smiled and said, "You should get it checked out."

Then I realized she was joking with me. She directed me to the twenty-first floor.

I should mention that when I'm anxious, I become disoriented. I've gotten lost so many times, I've learned to expect it, regardless of MapQuest, GPS, or personal directions. That day in the hospital was no different. I stepped out of the elevator on the twentieth floor instead of the twenty-first, found myself in obstetrics, and was asked, "Are you a new father?"

"No, I have prostate cancer."

"I'm sorry. Would you like to see your child?"

"I don't have a child."

"Your last name?"

"Michaels."

"Twins. How nice. One of our volunteers will take you in. If you'll just take a seat."

I realized I was in the wrong place and found the twenty-first floor before being given twins to hold. After a few more rounds of getting lost, I finally tracked down the meeting room.

Several metal folding chairs, a few overstuffed vinyl chairs, and a love seat that looked like a thrift-store bargain were spread around the room. Weight watchers, alcoholics, and cancer patients had occupied these seats. These stationary participants had heard war stories and absorbed the pain of their fellow attendees. I chuckled and thought to myself, *They're chair-a-pists.*

It was nearly 9:58 and I was the only one in the room. I didn't know whether to sit or stand. I looked out the window and saw irregular flat-roofed buildings dotting the skyline. This was Chicago, not San Francisco. I felt nostalgic for that beautiful city by the bay. I had spent over twenty years there establishing a psychiatric theater and being involved with a woman who broke my heart.

I told myself that if no one showed up soon, I would leave.

Suddenly, a very thin lady, wearing a pantsuit and a smile more artificial than saccharine, extended her hand, approached me, and said, "Hello. I'm Chaplain Merry. Are you here for the prostate group?"

I introduced myself and thought, *She's probably going to say an opening prayer and return to her duties.* I hoped that was all she was going to do, because I expected it to be an all-men's group. A woman couldn't possibly understand what I'd been through.

"Welcome. I'm the leader of the support group."

I felt dizzy and hoped I wouldn't pass out. Was I being sexist? Or were my feelings legitimate? They were legitimate, but were they accurate? Accurate, but were they skewed?

I was polite and didn't voice any of my thoughts. I had been taught to be "nice to strangers," or was it "never talk to strangers"? Maybe "only talk to polite strangers"? Whatever it was, I did not feel comfortable talking to this woman.

*Wasn't this supposed to be about a man's personal and private organs?* I thought.

"Would you like a cup of coffee?"

"Thanks, I'll get it."

"No, I insist."

I took the offered cup. I knew caffeine wasn't good for me, but I don't always do what's in my best interest. I sat down and took a sip. It was very hot and burned my tongue. It looked and tasted like brewed mud.

As I sat there, I wondered if this was going to be a one-to-one meeting led by a blond minister. All my religious beliefs and fears kicked in, and so did my anxiety, particularly when I realized that Chaplain Merry reminded me of Sister Cecilia, who had always been worried about the future of my soul. She should have been worried about the future of my prostate.

An older black man came in with his son. The father must have been in his eighties, and I guessed his son to be sixty-something. They greeted the chaplain, and she introduced Jerome and his son, Eugene. At four members, technically we were a group.

"Let's start the meeting," the chaplain said. "Today we will be talking about erogenous zones."

I nearly spilled my coffee.

"If someone touches one of your zones, you can get very stimulated. When my husband blows on my ear, I get so hot. It's *superlicious*."

She was trying, but no one was willing to talk about their erogenous zones. She switched topics.

"Has anyone had an erection lately?" she asked next.

"Last one was in 'eighty-two," Jerome said. "Over twenty years now."

"I almost had one," Eugene said, "but it only lasted thirty seconds."

"That's a beginning," Chaplain Merry said. "Would you care to elaborate?"

"Tried everything and kept trying until I finally gave up," Eugene added.

"Try rereading the chapter I assigned last time, and try to get your wife involved. It can really help."

I had had an erection recently. Was this something I wanted to share? Then I decided the point of the group was to share.

"I had one yesterday," I found myself saying.

"You did?" the chaplain said. "How long was it?"

*Did she want to know* inches *or* duration*?* I wondered. I was too embarrassed to ask her to clarify. I tried to explain. "It was ... it was—"

And then another man entered the room.

Hi, Richie," Jerome said. Richie looked like he might be in his late fifties: salt-and-pepper hair, big gut, somewhat distinguished.

"Had to finish up some work at the office."

"Ken was just talking about his erection," the chaplain explained.

"How long was it?" Richie asked. He looked directly at me and smiled.

I liked him immediately.

I learned that the chaplain had been running the group for the last two years and these guys were all regulars—an intimate group that talked about intimate topics. I stayed with the group for six weeks. I became more relaxed and began to share more. At times, it was informative; at others, intrusive. But it was always supportive. Eventually you realize you're not alone. The people there were sincere and wanted to help any way they could. I wish I had attended Us TOO meetings before my surgery. I'm sure it would have been very helpful. I would strongly recommend the group to anyone who is grappling with prostate cancer.

# 25. The Mind-Body Connection

As I mentioned earlier, getting an erection post-op was one of the best moments of my life. It took me back to adolescence, and although I certainly wasn't a teenager by any stretch of the imagination, I certainly felt like one. I was eager to see how much more I could do with my organ. Knowing I could have sex made me want to have it as much and as often as I could. I realized this wasn't logical. The more I thought about it, the more I wondered about the mind-body connection. I wondered how, specifically, the mind-body connection was connecting.

There has been a shift, by the way, from referring to this stage of recovery as overcoming impotence to penile rehabilitation. Part of the reasoning is that impotence has a negative connotation. I understand this, but I do think that it will take time for men to actually use this term. It may be more PC, but the phrase is long and awkward.

The truth is, most men don't even want to acknowledge anything associated with impotence, even through a more hopeful term like penile rehabilitation. But who knows? Times change and people do, too. In a caring environment, more men may feel comfortable talking about their sexual health in optimistic terms, post-prostate surgery, although I still wouldn't bet on penile rehabilitation as the term men would choose. Exact word choice doesn't matter, though, so long as the words are inclusive, supportive, and forward-looking.

On the internet forums, many men discussed pumps, injections, and implants and their concerns about each. I was glad my urologist didn't recommend any of these types of rehabilitation and wanted me to wait for nature to take its course. I know I was ignorant of my choices and only learned of them afterward, but I thank God for my timing, since the cancer had not spread and I am sexually functional.

I wonder if anyone has ever confronted routine forms of punishment inflicted by some urologists. I hadn't challenged my doctor about having a biopsy without anesthetic. I didn't know there was an alternative. Now I do.

What came first, the erection or the needle? In my case, it was the erection. Otherwise, I would have considered injections. That thought frightened me, but I had overcome many fears, including the biggest—having the operation—so I knew with time and work anything was possible. This mind-body connection was very clear.

I heard men say they couldn't go back to work because they were afraid of having accidents. Totally understandable. I went back to work after seven weeks of recovery. I couldn't watch another hour of TV or take another nap. Working, even part-time, was better than not working. The question seemed to be, *sanity or insanity*? I knew I needed to get back to a routine and being around people.

I returned with some trepidation about having an accident that would leak through. Worrying only encouraged self-fulfilling problems. I believe that the longer you treat yourself as a recovering patient, the longer you stay one.

Being at work kept me from worrying. Yes, everyone is different, and I don't have statistics to back up my claim that working is better than staying at home. That said, I personally believe that work actually helped me heal faster. It allowed me to be productive, to be part of a larger world, and it took my mind off my problems. For me *that* was the mind-body connection.

I mentioned that Dr. Kareful had prescribed a low dose of Viagra after surgery. I assumed I would be on it indefinitely. A year later, after being instructed by Mayo, I began seeing Dr. Strong again. He suggested that I stop taking Viagra.

"Why?" I asked.

"Fortunately, you don't have high blood pressure, but if you continue to take it, you could increase your chances of having a stroke or a heart attack."

"Should I take it at all?"

"Only if you need it."

*What a concept,* I thought to myself. *As needed. Why didn't I think of that?* After that, I experimented with Viagra, and I discovered I had less control of my bladder when I took it. I found it difficult to believe that I did not need it at all. The truth is I need it occasionally. Whether this is psychological or not isn't clear. I have tried not using it during sex; sometimes I function fine and other times I don't. Had I continued to go to Mayo, I'm sure I would have been given the same advice. My GP keeps in touch with Dr. Kareful regarding my PSA tests, and I receive letters from him saying he is glad to hear that I am doing well.

The general consensus seems to be that it is important to take one of the PDE5 inhibitors after surgery to help bring circulation back into the penis. I'm sure I was told that, but the truth is I felt I was going through so much during recovery, I couldn't retain all the information.

My question, though, is how important is it? What if not using drugs provides the same results? What if the body does a better job of healing itself? As time went on and my nerves healed from the surgery and the trauma, I found I could perform without drugs. Did I need Viagra to perform or not? This was a very difficult mind-body connection.

One of the side effects I had from taking a larger dose of Viagra was headaches. I learned to accept them, and I took Advil to relieve them. Many men report the same problem from the drug. Others have reported becoming flushed or suffering tinnitus (ringing in the ears). If not monitored, this damage can be permanent. Please read about side effects on the official Viagra website (https://www.viagra.com/learning/how-does-viagra-work). Cutting doses in half or switching to another drug (Cialis or Levitra) has helped others. Mind-body connection? Possibly. Definitely worth considering. Be sure to check with your doctor.

Erectionitis (my creative term for obsession about erections) is so pronounced that I have heard some men say pumps, drugs, and injections were ineffective. They *had* to get an implant. In fact, I have heard some men say that rather than bother with all the choices, they went directly for an implant after the surgery.

I know that would not be my choice. Most men who have prostatectomies are in their sixties or seventies. Some are in their fifties. I suppose it's all relative. Who am I to judge?

If you want an erection that badly, use a pump, check out injections, try all the drugs. Searching for the ultimate erection is as futile as searching for the Holy Grail. I'd rather spend my energy finding intimacy, which is more exciting than any form of sex. To me, that is the best mind-body connection.

# 26. Expectations

I wanted everything to be faster, from surgery to sex, but nature has its own timetable. Doctors give approximations because they really don't know. They really don't. Hard to believe, but true. I do think they try to be nonspecific but encouraging because they don't have answers for everything. Possible infections, improper healing, and disregarding instructions and orders can all play into the process. Unfortunately, we have become a litigious society wanting to find a source to blame for our problems. Doctors are careful about their language and their promises. Malpractice insurance is high for a reason.

I often asked myself, *Why don't my erections last? Why are my ejaculations dry? Will I ever feel comfortable about my new sexuality?*

There are so many other factors that contribute to the possibilities of erectile dysfunction. Once you age, let's say over sixty, your body starts to wear out. Plain and simple. Contributing factors such as high blood pressure, smoking, or obesity may cause or contribute to problems. Some other factors that may interfere are vascular disease, neurological disorders, diabetes, and thyroid disease.

One that gets very little mention is stress or depression. Both are difficult to measure and are often overlooked. A physician may ask you a few questions such as:

Have you been sleeping all right?

How is your appetite?

Are you able to concentrate?

These questions seem very simple and are often brushed off as insignificant. Yet they may lead to other questions, which can determine your level of tension. If you are anxious, you are going to have difficulty getting an erection. Fear of cancer can be a high stressor. Not having it can be relaxing.

Luckily, I now fall into the second category. My current PSA readings are less than .01, which is insignificant. I have been in remission for ten years, and I'm grateful I'm alive. I read posts in the forums about men happy to spend time with their families, enjoying the sunset and laughing with their loved ones.

Remember the importance of humor because it affords you perspective and objectivity. We have all experienced funny situations during our recovery. I'm sure all of you have gone through the flow test. I find it hard to believe that I'm the only guy who has "blitzed" his way through the bathroom: hitting walls, shower curtains, and, in my case, even the dog. I'm sure he wondered what I was doing. Finally, I sat down and laughed. I couldn't do anything else.

Another reminder that we can't control everything. In fact, we control very little. Sure, we can do Kegels, take time to heal, and hope and pray for the best. Prayer gives us hope, and hope keeps us alive. If things go differently than expected, we can learn to live with them. Great expectations often lead to humbling acceptances. Learn to go with the flow, literally.

# 27. Advice to Couples

Since I'm currently single, you might want to take my advice with a grain of salt. Actually, take it with a whole shaker.

Any adjustment after an operation is difficult. For men, prostate surgery is especially challenging. I do believe pre-op personality affects recovery behavior. If you were impatient or calm before, your demeanor will most likely be magnified after. You get where I'm going with this. This is true for any type of rehabilitation after surgery, especially if it is a traumatic one.

Often, patients blame their partners for their shortcomings. When I first heard this, I thought it was an isolated incident. When I heard it repeatedly, I saw it as a pattern. Your partner is not responsible for your performance. He or she is there to be caring and supportive during your recovery. You may be angry, frustrated, and despondent, but try not to take it out on your partner. Remember, both physical and psychological healing are occurring. If possible, I suggest couples counseling. If your partner won't join you, go for individual therapy. (Derrer, David, 2016).

Men, especially sixtysomethings and older, have been conditioned to play a certain role: that of the leader, provider, and protector. Not being able to do this can make one feel insecure and inadequate.

Nonverbal communication is important. I often recommend cuddling because it is a way to express closeness without words. It allows us to remember why we got together in the first place. Isn't that what intimacy is about? Knowing we are with someone we trust, who knows us—sometimes better than we know ourselves—someone we truly love.

A gentle touch can often mean more than any words. When your partner looks troubled or sad, a touch on the cheek or a squeeze of a hand can go a long way. Just staying in the same room and reading, listening to music, or doing a crossword can allow the other person to relax. It brings back a sense of normalcy or a sense of a remembered past. It allows the person to realize that things, although different, will return to a pattern: a different pattern, but one that still incorporates elements of a shared past. A sense that everything will be all right.

Allow yourself to grieve. Grieving is a process that needs to be completed. Many times it is done alone, but in my practice, I have seen couples come together over a shared loss. This loss may lead to discussion of other issues. Problems that have never been breached. In order to move on, these need to be resolved. Realize your partner is experiencing a loss he doesn't understand and can't define. He may not be able to verbalize his feelings, especially if he had problems doing so before.

"No kidding," you say. "He never put his emotions into words before, and now you're asking me to be even more patient." Yes, I am. He may not be able to articulate why he feels such a loss. He needs time to process the situation.

Grieving is difficult, and being able to express it may seem impossible. I know I felt sad for weeks. I couldn't quite understand it, but finally I stopped trying and accepted my grief. Once I did that, I cried. I cried because I had cancer, I didn't have a partner, and I had lost my mother. Some people might say, *That's self-pity. You need to get control of yourself and be a man.*

Men have always been told to act strong. Anything else is a sign of weakness. If we show vulnerability, we're considered sissies. But it's healthy to let go of stereotypes and let out pent-up emotion. Be there for him. If you see he is sad and depressed, hold him. Let him know you are there and that everything will be all right. Knowing you care is more important than you think. It allows the person to be himself. In time, some men recover their sexual functioning. If not, knowing you are there can make all the difference in his acceptance of himself.

Remember things that you shared and that still make you laugh. Bring up past trips, a party, or an incident you enjoyed that was specific to your relationship. Watch a movie, read a book together or to each other, look at photos.

You have more inner strength than you think. We all tend to underestimate ourselves. Remember you have each other and you will get through it.

# 28. An Ordinary Joe

I joined Prime Timers, a social group for older men. One of the members was having a Memorial Day picnic in his backyard. Men were sitting on metal chairs in the yard and the garage, the weather was pleasant, and everyone seemed relaxed. It was here that I met Joe.

He and I were sitting across from the buffet and he seemed to be a friendly guy. He was a bit overweight, had an expressive face, and was balding, probably in his seventies. He introduced himself and we chatted about weather and the party, and then we got to the topic of health.

"I had a prostatectomy a year ago," I said.

"I had one ten years ago," Joe responded.

"How did that go?" I asked. He had my full attention.

"All right," he answered.

"Can you have sex?" I asked, curious.

"You mean now or back then?"

"Both."

"I never got erect naturally before or after my prostate surgery."

"But were you able to get an erection eventually?"

"That reminds me of a funny story."

I smiled in anticipation. There were other men sitting within listening distance and anyone could have eavesdropped if they wanted to. But they were all involved in their own conversations.

"I had my surgery back in January 2000, and it was about six months after that. I went to my urologist because I still couldn't get an erection and I thought something was wrong. He recommended I try a drug called Caverject, also known as MUSE, so I thought I'd give it a shot," Joe said.

I nodded.

"After the doctor injected me in the office, I got an erection, and he said that should do it and mentioned the erection should last about an hour. I hadn't planned on having sex immediately after, since I went into the office looking for a solution, not anticipating an immediate erection."

"And?" I asked.

"Watch what you wish for."

I nodded.

"It's summer. I'm wearing shorts, and I have to go home by train. I bought a magazine to cover my erection, but the train was crowded and I had to hold on to a pole.

"And I'm not referring to mine."

We both laughed. The other guys at the party had heard us and soon they were laughing, too.

"The good news was it was what I wanted. The bad news was it lasted for four hours. I called my doc and he told me to take some Sudafed. Luckily that worked. I never tried it again and accepted not having an erection."

Our conversation gave me a whole different perspective on how important an erection was.

I met another Joe on the prostate forum. He had opted for an implant and decided to have it done in New York by a well-known specialist. At first, he was elated at the outcome and was happy to share the news. But the implant failed during the first year. Joe returned to the doctor, who was willing to do it again, but Joe no longer trusted him and had his colleague do it. After a short time, it too failed. Joe was deeply depressed and even talked about suicide. I kept in touch with him until he saw a therapist, who helped him. Joe eventually got a third implant, and it was successful.

*Would I have the nerve for self-injections or an implant?* I wondered. *Is getting an erection that important?* I thought for a few minutes and decided it was. I was still young. I had just turned sixty-five.

## 29. Reality Check

Recently I had to take a bus to go to friend's birthday celebration. Riding on public transportation was both practical and convenient. But I was running late, and I hoped I hadn't just missed a bus and then would have to wait even longer. I got to the corner and saw a group of seven people waiting. I looked down the street—no bus in sight. It was then that I took a good look at my fellow travelers.

A nicely dressed woman in her forties was seated in a motorized wheelchair, speaking fluent Spanish with a younger man, and they were having a friendly and animated conversation.

The first thought that went through my head was, *Great, it's going to take even longer because the driver will have to lower the handicap ramp in order for her to get on.* I immediately regretted thinking this, since it was so selfish and unkind.

When the bus finally arrived, she got on in record time, using her upper body effectively. I realized she was paralyzed from the waist down. Someone prepared a space for her, and she quickly maneuvered herself into the spot. I sat at a window seat, two rows adjacent to her. Once settled, she waved cheerfully, throwing kisses to her friend who had helped her on.

I saw past her handicap and realized she was a person with a life much more difficult than mine. She hadn't let her limitations define her. She didn't seem bitter or disgruntled. In fact, she seemed to be doing better than the rest of us.

As often happens when a bus is late, there was a crowd at each stop. At the next stop, a woman with a shopping cart filled with groceries got on. She pushed back a disabled seat and squeezed herself and her cart in the space so that people could pass. The bus was packed now, and no one could move. Even if I wanted to give up my seat, I couldn't. I had forgotten to bring a book, so I continued to people watch.

Two more stops and an elderly Asian man got on, carrying a heavy grocery bag in one hand and a cane in the other. A man wearing a US Marine Corps cap yelled, "*Stop picking up people. There isn't any more room!*" But when has a bus driver listened to his passengers? Another passenger helped the woman move her grocery cart so that the disabled man could sit. Somehow she managed to maneuver herself and her cart off at the next stop.

Everything seemed to fall into place, but then two more people got on with carts, and I was sure there would be problems. One young guy took out his bags, placed them on the storage rack, and folded up his cart. The woman who came on next had a larger cart than the previous passenger, and although she was able to get past the wheelchair, she was unable to get any farther because of all the obstacles. The traffic jam on the bus rivaled anything on the road, and the bus had started to move. People were stuck between the door, the carts, and the wheelchair. At that moment, the marine tried to help the lady with the full grocery cart squeeze in behind him. He couldn't stand up, but he reached out to help her. She couldn't speak English and was frightened and upset. But the marine kept trying, even though he wasn't able to help in all the ways he wanted to.

Although I was wedged in, I managed to stand up, reach across, and pull the cart in a few inches. Somehow, we all made it work. We exchanged a few smiles, and the bus continued on its way. Eventually, the woman in the wheelchair got off. At the next stop, the woman with the grocery cart got off. Finally, the marine signaled for his stop, got up, and used two steel canes to maneuver down the aisle. He moved toward the exit, but before he got off, he tipped his hat to me and said, "Semper fi." There hadn't been any indication he was handicapped. I smiled back, and soon the bus was back to its normal load, dropping people off at their appointed stops.

I'll never forget that trip because I learned a very important lesson. Initially, I had been upset because I thought someone in a wheelchair would inconvenience me. After my ride, I found myself not caring about being late.

Having cancer, poor erections, and no partner all paled in comparison to what I had just experienced. I was not a disabled ex-marine, who probably lost his ability to walk freely while fighting for our country.

Whenever you think you're having problems, get out there. If you feel well enough, volunteer in your community. Experience life. Not life with all the conveniences we have at our disposal, but life in the *real lane*. When I finally sat down with my friends at a nice restaurant, I was happy not only for the person celebrating his birthday. I was happy that I'd been able to get there on my own. My cancer seemed so insignificant; I had forgotten all about it.

# 30. Patience, Patience, Patience

Five months after my operation, my incisions began to heal, and I began feeling more energetic.

But recovery is a marathon, not a sprint. When I did too much, my body let me know. I reminded myself that I must be patient and allow my body to continue its healing. The only permission I needed was mine.

I had begun seeing some of my patients again, and each one asked about my health and recovery. Their concern was comforting, and I welcomed the synergy they provided.

After work, I found I was exhausted, both physically and emotionally. I returned phone calls but tried to keep them short. If a patient was going through recuperation, I'd say, "Take care of *yourself* and use your energy to heal." I tried to heed my own advice and found it wasn't easy. A good example of "the cobbler going barefoot."

I was still processing the fact that I had had cancer. It had taught me how tenuous life is. Most of us who are in good health take it for granted. I know I did. "Life is short" took on new meaning for me.

The fact that I'm still here is one part luck and two parts miracle. I have learned to forgive faster and more often; to find humor in situations that once made me angry; and, most important, to go with the flow. These maxims have made my life much easier. Unfortunately, it took cancer to enlighten and transform me.

After surgery, I had a PSA test every three months for the first eighteen months. After that, I had and still do have the test every six months. Whenever I do, the result is the same: an undetectable level (<.01), indicating no evidence of recurrent disease.

I was very lucky to have my cancer detected early. I am not religious, but I do consider myself spiritual. In other words, I need God. I believe I was brought into this world for a reason, and it may have been to write this book. To spread the message to as many men as possible that prostate cancer is serious but not necessarily deadly. The solution is simple: EARLY DETECTION. I will preach that message the rest of my life. I regularly find myself asking men when their last physical was, if it included a prostate exam, and what their PSA score is.

It is time for men to become proactive about their health, especially regarding prostate cancer screening. Each time I bring up anything associated with men's health, I am usually met with embarrassment and hushed whispers. I was probably the same before my diagnosis, and I recognize the behavior. We need to begin a dialogue, whether through planned awareness (media), campaigns, or education.

Open, honest, and respectful conversations about sexuality and sexual health are rare in our society. The same was true with AIDS, and many people died as a result. Communicating starts by sharing your experience with another man and letting him know that it's all right to talk about it.

Cancer empowered me. It gave me new appreciation for life and the strength to deal with it. It made me realize that if I could get through it, I could get through anything. My illness taught me to take risks and to stop wasting time worrying.

Take it from a therapist who knows: recovering from cancer doesn't mean everything else will fall into place, including your relationships, your goals, and your future. Nothing is guaranteed, and although this can be daunting, it can also motivate us to keep striving to shape our future, make our lives better, and, in turn, maybe improve the lives of those around us.

This book is about using humor to live with disease, specifically prostate cancer. And humor includes not taking everything so seriously, especially yourself. You too may find yourself blitzing, at the Diaper Depot, or even at a Kegel class.

Always remember our generation paved the way for social change, and we will continue to do the same with health and longevity. Never give up the fight.

# Epilogue

## Ten Years, a Few Months, and a Hundred Years Later

Some people consider a cancer diagnosis their epilogue, but I consider it my prologue. Yes, I am still cancer-free as of my most recent PSA test, which was on July 21, 2018.

I still struggle with stress and chaos. Other changes include travel (more); job (less); and my future (who knows?). I have moved from Chicago to Key West, where I've lived for the last seven years.

I've arrived at the conclusion that God manifests the divine in the form of love. And with that, I try to love as much as I can.

Although I'm lucky to have survived these years without problems, I no longer seize the day; I seize each and every moment.

Our time here is relatively short. I'm trying to make the most of it, and I urge you to do the same.

Living well and doing what I love are key for me and could be for you, too.

# REFERENCES

Benson, J. T., Fotham, E. T. H., Godley, P. A., Ivanonova, A., Michel, M., Mohler, J. L., Schroder, J. C., Smith, G. J., and Su, J. L. 2006. The North Carolina-Louisiana Prostate Cancer Project (PCaP). *Prostate*, 66: 1162–1176.

Carlsson, S., Holmstrom, B., Hugosson, J., Jonsson, H., Lilja, H., Stattin, P., and Vickers, A. 2014. "Prostate Cancer Mortality in Areas with High and Low Prostate Cancer Incidence." *Journal of the National Cancer Institute*, 106(8): 193.

Derrer, David. 2016. "Coping with Erectile Dysfunction." WebMD. https://www.webmd.com.

Fisher, Terri D., Moore, Zachary T., and Pittenger, Mary-Jo. 2012. "Sex on the Brain?" *Journal of Sex Research*, 49(1): 69–77.

McHargue, Ryan. 2017. "Caverject vs. Trimix." Healthfully. https://healthfully.com.

Seaman, Andrew. 2017. "Does Penis Length Recover After Prostate Removal?" Reuters Health News.

Stiller, Ben. 2016. "Ben Stiller opens up for the first time since revealing cancer diagnosis." *Today*. https://www.today.com/video/ben-stiller-on-prostate-cancer-and-the-psa-test-every-guy-should-get-tested-815118915716?v=railb.

# RESOURCES

## Malecare

www.malecare.org

Go-to group for prostate cancer patients. Website includes information about the latest trials as well as support groups, blogs, and forums.

## Us TOO

www.ustoo.org

Group founded by prostate-cancer patients: features forums and current information about prostate cancer.

## Viagra

https://www.viagra.com/learning/how-does-viagra-work

The official Viagra website: includes general information, cautions, and details regarding potential side effects.

## WebMD

www.webmd.com

Good resource for Kegel exercises and their use to help manage and improve male urinary incontinence.

## ACKNOWLEDGMENTS

Although at times this book was a real challenge, I was blessed to have a dedicated professional team and a supportive group of friends and family that encouraged me to press forward.

I would like to thank my dream team of Diane Aronson, editing coordinator; Karen Minster, interior designer; Laura Duffy, cover designer; Sandra Smith, copy editor; Janet Rosenberg, proofreader; Sean Michaels, website designer; and consultants, Adrienne Curran, MD, and Jerry Jackson, MD. Thank you also to Claire Petrie for reading early chapters of the manuscript.

A special thanks to my friends and family, Lynne, Susanna, Patrick, Shelli, Butch, Tom, Chris, Cindy, Judy, Edgardo, Wesley, Mark, Russell, and Lori. Special acknowledgments go to Us TOO; all the prostate cancer patients who shared their stories with me; and to my incredible urologist, R. Jeffrey Karnes, MD, his team, and all the staff at Mayo Clinic.

Without you, this book would not have been possible. I am extremely grateful and thankful to you all.

Made in the USA
Lexington, KY
30 August 2019